STUDENT AND CHIEF

The Osler-Camac Correspondence

Photograph of Osler which Camac used as the frontispiece for the
notebooks containing his correspondence with Osler.

STUDENT AND CHIEF
The Osler-Camac Correspondence

Arranged, edited, introduced and annotated

by

EARL F. NATION, M.D.

Past-President, American Osler Society,

Pasadena, California

and

JOHN P. McGOVERN, M.D.

Past-President, American Osler Society,

Houston, Texas

1980

THE CASTLE PRESS, PASADENA, CALIFORNIA

THE OSLER-CAMAC LETTERS are the property of the Medical Library of the Los Angeles County Medical Association. They are published with the permission of the Library Committee and of Mrs. Elizabeth Crahan, the Librarian, in an edition of one thousand copies.

Table of Contents

BIBLIOMANIACS:

Cherishers of Biographical Records

THE MEN I SPEAK OF (bibliomaniacs) keep alive
in us an interest in the great men of the past,
and not alone in their works, which they cher-
ish, but in their lives, which they emulate.
They would remind us continually that in the
records of no other profession is there to be
found so large a number of men who have
combined intellectual pre-eminence with no-
bility of character.*

*From *John Locke as a Physician,* an address delivered
by Osler before the Students' Societies of the Medical
Department of the University of Pennsylvania, January
16, 1900. (*Lancet,* London, 2: 1115-1123, 1900.)

Used by Camac as the opening quotation in *Counsels
and Ideals from the Writings of William Osler.*

Introduction

"IN THE continual remembrance of a glorious past individuals and nations find their noblest inspiration." This quotation along with hundreds of others and much longer excerpts from Osler's more philosophical, historical, and biographical essays, are preserved in a small book, long out of print, *Counsels and Ideals from the Writings of William Osler* by C. N. B. Camac.

Charles Nicoll Bancker Camac, an eminent physician in his own right, was one of many whose lives and careers were profoundly touched by the genius of William Osler. Beginning in 1896, he spent one year as an Assistant Resident in Medicine under Osler at Johns Hopkins Hospital in Baltimore. This brief acquaintance led not only to the "Counsels and Ideals" but also to a lasting relationship and frequent correspondence that continued until Osler's death in 1919.*

In this present volume, the personal correspondence between Osler, the *chief*, and Camac, the *student*, has been collated, annotated, edited, and published to help recall and further document a segment of "the continual remembrance of a glorious

*See Appendix 1, page 119, for Camac's contribution to the *Sir William Osler Memorial Volume*, written seven years after Osler's death, which gives additional insight and perspective to their relationship.

past," that particular era being the so-called "heroic age" of modern American medicine, and for other pleasing and valid reasons as well. Primary amongst these is to reveal again the unique nature of William Osler, often referred to as the "Father of Modern American Medicine," through his continuous and inspiring correspondence with just one disciple, Charles Camac. It provides us with a superb illustration of an enduring friendship of the type that Osler maintained with scores of his former students and colleagues. It also reveals to us his style, warmth with brevity, pervasive humanism and how, by example, these traits rubbed off on his students.

Another reason for this present effort is the timing of its publication for we intend for its arrival to coincide with the celebration of the Tenth Anniversary of the American Osler Society. We believe that this volume will be of particular interest to Oslerians everywhere.

Camac had apparently intended to publish his correspondence with Osler sometime before his death on September 27, 1940. In a posthumous biographical sketch, A. G. Beaman[1] wrote: "During the last months of his life Dr. Camac was engaged in putting together a volume of Sir William Osler's letters to him with interspersed commentary — which regrettably was not finished." He added, "It is hoped that Mrs. Camac will see that this project is carried to completion." This was never done. The collection of letters, along with books and other correspondence, notably from Harvey Cushing, the eminent neurosurgeon, found its way after her death into the hands of rare book dealers in Pasadena, California. From these dealers the Medical Library of the Los Angeles County Medical Association acquired the collection. The collected material, contained in three large, loose-leafed notebooks,** comprises a treasure-trove of Osleriana.

This book is concerned with the contents of the first two notebooks, which contain thirty-nine handwritten and sixty-three typewritten letters from William Osler to Camac. There is a photocopy of another, as well as eight calling cards with handwritten notes, six postal cards, and five telegrams. Also, there are twenty-five holograph letters from Lady Osler to Camac, two from her sister, Mrs. Susan R. Chapin, and one from Osler's niece, Amy Gwyn (later Mrs. Thomas McCrae). Camac also included thirteen of his own letters to the Oslers. There are four related letters from William Sydney Thayer, Camac's immediate predecessor and senior as Resident Physician in Medicine at Johns Hopkins.

The first two notebooks also contain miscellaneous material related to events covered in the Osler correspondence. This includes six letters from Thomas R. Boggs relating to a gift of the 1683 edition of Browne's *Certain Miscellany Tracts* by some of his former students and friends to Osler. There also are included the preface and a page from the auction dealer's catalogue describing this book, along with letters from the Surgeon General's Librarian and the Librarian of the New York Academy of Medicine relating to it. Correspondence from Humphrey Milford, of the Oxford University Press, relating to Camac's book, *Counsels and Ideals from the Writ-*

**See Appendix 2, page 121, for description of the contents of Volume 3.

ings of William Osler, and other miscellaneous letters to Camac such as two from Miss Olean Humpton, Osler's long-time secretary in Baltimore, are also included.

The correspondence is arranged in chronological order. The Osler letters were numbered by Camac in blue pencil, more or less in chronological sequence. Since many of the letters bear no complete date, Camac, in arranging them chronologically in later years, made some mistakes. An effort has been made to correct these errors and to date the letters as accurately as possible. Some of the letters bear brief notations in Camac's hand.

In an address "The Basis of Sir William Osler's Influence on Medicine,"[2] Dr. Wilburt C. Davison, organizer and first Dean of the Duke Medical School, a former Rhodes Scholar under Osler, and the first Honorary Member of the American Osler Society, after stating that "Osler was the most human of human beings that I have ever known," listed the seven pillars upon which Osler's fame rested.

These were first, as a physician; second, as a teacher; third, as a scientist; fourth, as a medical reformer; fifth, as a medical writer; sixth, as a humanist; and seventh, as a personality. Davison said of Osler in terms of the seventh pillar:

> Those who knew him firsthand, and this included all who knew him even briefly, felt the warmth and glow of his presence, and were a devoted, almost an apostolic band. If their zeal was at times overlavish . . . their motivation was honest. Though Osler, unlike Atlas, never stopped to shoulder the world, he always kept his arms around it.

He exuded familiarity tempered with reserve. He could take the arm of the most exalted without arousing resentment, but no one took his arm or slapped him on the back. He did what comes naturally, he followed the Golden Rule, and his creed was to like and sympathize with everyone. He never gave a thought to the length of his own shadow. If he could not see good in people, he saw nothing. In any gathering, he seemed able to address each guest intimately—Tom, Jack, Jim, or whatever familiarity dictated. Osler's wonderful power made every young man he met feel that he was in the presence of one who was taking a personal interest in him. It was a true and natural expression of the overflowing humanity that was part of him. Universal sympathy was the essence of his greatness, a greatness of personality, that characteristic power to perceive and elicit the best in any companion.

Indeed, through his unique blend of word and example, Osler influenced not only the course of American medicine, but enriched and gave direction to the lives and careers of each of those who studied under him. He was the model of the complete physician: supremely competent in the science of medicine, humane and constantly aware of the uniqueness of each patient, cognizant of the physician's larger role in society. To be an Osler student was to be privileged to take part in a profound and lasting experience that transcended the boundaries of formal education.

As one savors the following correspondence, he will sense each of these qualities of which Davison wrote — and note how they flowered in Osler's student.   E.F.N.
                                                        J.P.M.

STUDENT AND CHIEF

The Osler-Camac Correspondence

Camac's Residency Days
1896-1897

CHARLES CAMAC was born in Philadelphia on August 6, 1868, to William and Ellen McIlvain Camac, a family of well-known Pennsylvania Quakers. After spending a year at Guy's Hospital Medical School in London, he entered medical school at the University of Pennsylvania in 1895, one year after William Osler left for Johns Hopkins. Upon graduation he interned at Johns Hopkins Hospital and in 1896 became Assistant Resident in Medicine under Osler. This service terminated one year later when Camac moved to New York City to enter practice with his brother-in-law, Henry D. Nicoll.

From 1899 to 1905 Camac served as director of the laboratory of clinical pathology in the Cornell Medical School. He served as Instructor in Medicine, then lecturer, and, finally, as Professor of Clinical Medicine at Cornell between 1905 and 1910. After 1906 he no longer accepted private patients in order to devote all of his energy to academic work. In 1910 Camac transferred to Columbia University's College of Physicians and Surgeons as Assistant Professor of Clinical Medicine. Here he remained until 1934.

During the First World War, Camac served in the

United States Army Medical Corps, achieving the rank of Lieutenant Colonel (Fig. 1). He was medical chief of General Hospital No. 38 at Eastview, New York, when he retired from military service in July, 1919.

Camac married Julia Augusta Metcalf on November 17, 1897. The Camacs had two daughters, Harriet, who later married Dr. John E. Elmendorf, and Eva, who became Mrs. Frederick Harvey Isitt.

After the death of his first wife, Camac married Miss Christie M. Fraser of Tuxedo Park, New York, on May 25, 1935. He then retired to Altadena, California where he died on September 27, 1940. He and his second wife are buried at San Gabriel Cemetery in San Gabriel, California.

Dr. Camac's home and possessions were left to his second wife's sister, Miss A. Bertha Fraser. It was she who disposed of the correspondence with which this writing is concerned through the Yale and Brown Bookshop in Pasadena, California.

The correspondence between the Oslers and Camac began early in the year of Camac's assistant residency. The first piece was a brief clinical note, handwritten on blue stationery imprinted "1 West Franklin St." Camac has pencilled in the date, 1896 (Fig. 2). The "Nux" referred to is nux vomica, formerly much used as a tonic.

Dear Dr. Camac, Mrs. Williams is an old friend & patient who was with her husband (Ward C) in 1889. Do not take her history—I have it. Let her take Nux. & she can rest in bed until 12 daily.

Yours, W. Osler

Another brief, undated note, written on a tiny slip of paper and addressed to either Thayer or Camac, followed. It said succinctly:

Please send me over the Bronardel on Typhoid Fever.

Yours, W. Osler

There followed another note on 1 West Franklin St. white stationery that Camac has dated the same year, 1896.

Dear Camac, Take Dr. Fox around with you and show him the interesting cases. He is a good man—good enough to make a diagnosis of myxoedema.

(Unsigned)

Showing that Osler's interest in his residents extended beyond professional concerns was a note from Mrs. Osler on her card (Fig. 3):

Dear Dr. Camac, I hope you will come in for tea Friday afternoon at 5 o'clock—quite informally to meet Misses Gwyn[3] from Canada.

Sincerely, G. R. Osler

The first fully dated letter in the collection concerns, as Camac has noted, his visit to England (Fig. 4).

11-5-96

Dear Dr. Broadbent,[4] Would you give Dr. Camac, one of my assistants, an opportunity to see any of your Hospital patients under Schotts treatment.[5] I am trying to introduce it with us.

Yours, respectfully, Wm. Osler

The first typewritten letter is on Osler's 1 West Franklin Street office stationery, which notes his consultation hours as 3-5 PM.

1-14-97

Dear Camac: I want to go over tomorrow all of the photographs to pick out one of a case of scleroderma which we had in the hospital some years ago (1891).

Please at the same time give me a memorandum of your expenses about the Nauheim trip.[6]

Sincerely yours, Wm. Osler

Camac has appended the following note: "The generous offer was of course not accepted — yet he would have personally defrayed expenses incurred for the hospital and this I knew."

Osler frequently called upon Camac for aid in finding material for articles and diagnoses. On January 15, 1897 came a terse typewritten request:

Dear Camac: Will you please get for me tomorrow the history of James Cotter or Cutter, who had scleroderma of his legs.

Sincerely yours, Wm. Osler

In 1898 Osler's paper "On Diffuse Scleroderma," with special reference to the use of the thyroid gland extract, was published in the *Journal of Cutaneous and Genitourinary Diseases.*[7]

Other requests followed:

Dr. William Osler
No. 1 West Franklin Street, Baltimore
Feb. 5th, 1897

Dear Camac: There is a photograph of a very emaciated woman who showed the abdominal aorta. Could you find it for me?

Sincerely yours, Wm. Osler

Dr. William Osler
No. 1 West Franklin Street, Baltimore
May 14th, 1897

Dear Dr. Camac: I want two cases of movable spleen, both of which were operated on. One was a case of pulsating pleurisy in a woman in Ward G, with *twisting of the spleen*, some four or five years ago. Her history had a good diagram. Then there was a woman in Ward C. Bloodgood might have them both. I want all the photographs illustrating abdominal tumors, and those drawings showing patterns of the abdominal tumidity.

If there is no regular lecture for the post-graduates tomorrow, will you put up a notice, please, that I will lecture at twelve o'clock in the amphitheater on the medical anatomy of the abdomen?

Sincerely yours, Wm. Osler

Camac has noted that these cases were to be used in the preparation of Osler's monograph on abdominal tumors.[8]

There is one handwritten request addressed to Thayer,[9] as follows:

Dear Thayer Dr. Gray of Winston has been failing in health & strength. The left lobe of the liver seems a little large & nodular. Will you take him into the Private Ward for a week or so & take the blood, etc.

Camac adds a cryptic note: "pernicious anemia case. Died in Ward C."

In the summer of 1897, on the 1 West Franklin St. personal stationery, came the following holographic letter:

Dear Camac, Thayer, I suppose is away. He said he was going to the country. If Mrs. McIlray's child is all peeled they can go. I should think she could get off by this time.

And, on August 5, 1897, while the Oslers were away from Baltimore there came the letter which has been reproduced elsewhere[10] and which concerned Camac's decision to leave Johns Hopkins (Fig. 5).

[On Vacation][11] Aug. 5th [97]

Dear Camac: I am so sorry to hear that you think of leaving us. We shall miss you very much. Your qualities of method and neatness supplement so well the absence of these features in several of us that we shall find it very hard to replace you. Of course the chance is too good to refuse & you should be able to get an assistantship at one of the schools or in the post-graduate. I will send you, or give you, letters to the men who may be most useful in this respect. I shall be back early in Sept. after the Montreal meeting & we can talk over the situation. Then if you hear of any positions available in N.Y. let me know. I have friends in all the faculties & might be of use.

Mrs. Osler tells me to say that she is extremely sorry to hear of your intended departure.

Sincerely yours, Wm. Osler

An undated letter that had to have been written around the middle of August 1897 congratulates Camac on his engagement. In this letter Osler also expresses his excitement over the finding by W. G. MacCallum[12] of the method by which malaria parasites propagate in the blood of crows. MacCallum was a recent Hopkins graduate so Osler was doubly gratified by the reception of MacCallum's work at a meeting of the British Association for the Advancement of Science held in Toronto, and presided over by Lister, who had recently been elevated to the peerage.

[1897]

Dear Camac: I shall reach Baltimore on Saturday about noon—come in to lunch. Many congratulations on your engagement. We are both delighted. I had the pleasure of meeting Dr. Metcalf many years ago; he & Howard were old chums. Make no final arrangement about the wards until I come. It will only be a few days after the 1st and we can begin on the Monday. This find of MacCallum's in the crows blood is of the greatest interest—evidently conjugation of distinct elements of which the flagella are the important ones.

Love to all the boys.

Yours, Wm. Osler

This ends the preserved correspondence between the Chief and one of his trainees during the year of his assistanceship. Camac notes on the final letter that, "Dr. O. gave a dinner, of all the attendings & staff of all departments, at an hostelry as a farewell to me." Such attention to his students, even a one-year assistant, was another of Osler's endearing characteristics.

Camac left Johns Hopkins in October, 1897, to be succeeded by McCrae.[13] Osler wrote to Thayer, "—lucky we have so good a man."

Correspondence followed later in 1897 concerning a paper on cholecystitis on which Camac had been working. This was written by hand on Osler's personal stationery.

1 West Franklin St.
['97]

Dear Camac: When will I expect a proof of your paper? Will you deal with the cholecystitis fully and take the cases I gave in the paper on Hepatic Complications (Tr.Ed.

Med.Jr.) of T.F.; I shall then speak *only* of the hepatic features.

Sincerely yours, Wm. Osler

On November 7, 1897, Osler acknowledged receipt of the paper.

1 West Franklin St.
11 . 7 . 97

Dear Camac: Mss. received—many thanks. It will make a bully article & do you good. I am not sure how the N.Y. Jr. will like the tables. I will ask Foster.

Much regret that I cannot see you off. Many blessings on you both.

Yours, Wm. Osler

Correspondence During Hopkins Days

before Osler accepted appointment as
Regius Professor of Medicine at Oxford

1897-1905

AFTER a hiatus of six months Osler resumes the correspondence with a typewritten note:

> *No. 1 W. Franklin Street, Baltimore*
> *May 13th, 1898*

Dear Camac: I have written to Thompson[14] and Stimson,[15] and I hope something may come of it. I am sure that you could give great satisfaction. It was very nice indeed to see you.

> *Sincerely yours, Wm. Osler*

Three days later there came another brief type-written letter on Osler's new office letterhead expressing his pleasure at the outcome.

> *No. 1 W. Franklin Street, Baltimore*
> *May 16th, 1898*

Dear Camac: I am very glad to hear from Gilman Thompson today that you have been appointed instructor of clinical microscopy. I am sure that you will make it a great success.

> *Sincerely yours, Wm. Osler*

Osler's new letterhead stated "Consultation hours, 2:30-4:30," instead of the previous "3-5."

With Osler's help Camac thus was launched at Cornell. Two days later another brief typewritten letter offering encouragement arrived.

> *No. 1 W. Franklin Street, Baltimore*
> *May 18, 1898*

Dear Camac: I feel sure that you will be able to make a great deal of the position and make the course very attractive. If you once get a good laboratory well started you could constantly have a number of nice graduates working with you.

> *Sincerely yours, Wm. Osler*

Ten days later Osler wrote again.

> *No. 1 W. Franklin Street, Baltimore*
> *May 28th, 1898*

Camac: Thanks for the list of tumor cases, which is very interesting.

Very glad indeed to hear of the appointment. I am sure you will be able to make clinical microscopy a very favorite subject in New York, where, I believe, it has never had a proper consideration.

> *Sincerely yours, Wm. Osler*

From New York Camac wrote Osler during the spring of 1898. The Oslers were about ready to depart for England and Camac was worrying, with some prescience, about whether the attractions there might be too beguiling. He wrote, "I hear of your plans for a long European visit — I hope Britania will not coquette you into forgetfulness of the simple Columbia — we want you to take an after school hours play but those are such dangerously fascinating fields. With remembrances to the family. Believe me very sincerely yours, C.N.B. Camac."

The move, however, was eight years away.

The next correspondence from Osler to Camac concerned Camac's progress at Cornell.

> *1 West Franklin St., Baltimore, Md.*
> *Oct. 31, '98*

Dear Camac: I was very glad to get your letter today & to hear that you are all right & in good condition. The news about the school [Cornell] is very reassuring. I feel confident that it will be a great success. I hope they have arranged in the Dispensary for teaching rooms as well as for a small laboratory. The latter is a very good suggestion. We shall try to get it this next year, when we enlarge the class-room.

> *Sincerely yours, Wm. Osler*

Several months later came a warm and enthusiastic handwritten letter from Baltimore.

> *2-9-99*

Dear Camac; So glad to hear from you. I am sure the clinical microscopy work will tell. It is most attractive for the students and young doctors. So glad of the gallbladder article. It will do too for our third Typhoid studies at which I am at last at work. I have been much driven this winter—so much on hand and so many calls. By the way look out for the mild cases of trichinosis at Bellevue—the eosinophilia is most remarkable. Thayer has just found a 6th case in a nurse in town. It is really a very good blood find—you remember one of the cases when you were here. The associate Professor is doing so well—a good many calls out of town. We still miss you and your good system. The new school I hope will make progress. Schurman[16] was here a few weeks ago—full of hope & plans. Mrs. O & Ike[17] are well—I hope to see you at an early date. I have only hurried thro. N.Y. in my last three visits.

Kind regards to your wife & to Dr. Metcalf.[18] Mrs. Osler sends love.

Yours ever, Wm. Osler

After a hiatus of ten months there came a typed letter from 1 W. Franklin Street.

Jan. 3, 1900

Dear Camac: A Happy New Year to you. Very glad you liked the photograph. I hope you are getting well into harness. I hear of you occasionally & am constantly promising myself the pleasure of a visit to you.

I think after that article your present title would be sufficient, and the Formerly Assistant Resident Physician Johns Hopkins Hospital.

With kind regards to Mrs. Camac.

Sincerely yours, Wm. Osler

The next letter was written by hand and was rather sad.

April 6, 1900

Dear Camac: I am very sorry to hear of the death of your father. From what you say of your relatives it must be a loss of exceptional severity. But it must have been a great satisfaction to him to feel that you were so comfortably settled in life and doing so well.

I have had that horrid disease the influenza for the first time. I am better now but rather used up. Revere & Mrs. Osler keep well. I hope we may see you in the Spring.

With sincere regards.

Yours ever, Wm. Osler

The next friendly note is written from abroad.[19]

From the Gwyle, Swanage
viii-23-00

Dear Camac: I returned yesterday. It would be delightful to see you & Mrs. Camac here. I wish that I could put you up for the night, or indeed for a week—but our only spare room is occupied. We shall be here all next week— Do come over. With kindest regards to your good angel.

Sincerely yours, Wm. Osler

There is a lapse of a year before the next letter which was typewritten.

1 W. Franklin Street, Baltimore
April 12, 1901

Dear Camac: I think several of our men are going up for the City Hospital examinations.

It was very nice to see Dr. Metcalf in Thomasville. I also saw Dr. Thomas.[20] It will be delightful to see you here at the end of the month. You must give us an evening.

With love to Mrs. Camac.

Sincerely yours, Wm. Osler

After spending a good part of the summer in England, Osler wrote about various matters, including books, on September 12, 1901. He used stationery from one of the places he visited, Incheven, North Berwick, but scratched this out on the letterhead.

12-9-01

Dear Camac: How delightful to hear the news about the little passenger. Good luck to her! It was very sad to hear of your sister's death. You had not the address in the letter you sent me so that I did not know where to write until after we had returned from Holland where the Doctor (to whom I had written) sent it. She made a brave fight.

We should get in the 21st. I think the Jamaica man

had better come down to Baltimore as I shall go thro. to Wilkesbarre with Mrs. O. & the boy. I have got some treasures in the way of old books, — a few gems & many good solid works of the masters.

With love & best wishes to your good wife.

Sincerely yours, Wm. Osler

Some references in the correspondence are cryptic, such as the book and the meeting referred to in the next letter written six weeks later.

1 W. Franklin Street, Baltimore
Oct. 30th, 1901

Dear Camac: I knew you would like the book. It is perfectly charming.

I had heard of the dinner to Thomas, but have had no official notice. I shall be very glad indeed to subscribe, as he is a man for whom I have the greatest regard.

Don't forget that you are to come down to one of our meetings.

Sincerely yours, W. Osler

The following month there came a letter from Osler that was in obvious response to one from Camac. It is typed but contains a holographic "Love to Mrs. Camac" at the bottom.

1 W. Franklin Street, Baltimore
Nov. 21st, 1901

Dear Camac:—Thanks for your note. The Stout child's case is an interesting one. Thanks for looking after her. Mr. Stout's address is Mr. James H. Stout, Menomonie, Wisconsin.

I am much interested in the data about the hospitals. I am trying to collect statistics from the different cities. I feel that an entirely new deal should be made in the matter of the teaching of clinical medicine.

Sincerely yours, Wm. Osler

There followed within two weeks a personal, handwritten note relating to the birth of Camac's daughter:

> *1 West Franklin St.*
> *XII-5-01*

Dear Camac: Your note of the 30th with the welcome news I found this p.m. on my return from Michigan.[21] Many congratulations! Love to Mother & Child.

> *Yours ever, W. Osler*

A short time later Osler responded professionally to a letter by Camac that obviously related to the emerging importance of the recent recognition of the acid fast organism. This letter again was typed by a secretary who did not identify herself but presumably was Osler's long-time stenographer, Miss B. O. Humpton.

> *No. 1 W. Franklin Street, Baltimore*
> *Dec. 10th, 1901*

Dear Camac: The point you raise is a very interesting one. I listened with great interest to the whole discussion at the Tuberculosis Congress[22] on these acid-fast bacilli which are evidently much more widely spread than we had been in the habit of supposing, and it may lead us to reconsider whether one or two bacilli mean specifically tuberculosis.

I wish you would add a few marginal notes in your copy of my text book for corrections, etc. They are very useful and helpful.

Give my love to Mrs. Camac and the baby.

> *Sincerely yours, Wm. Osler*

A note by Camac on the above letter said, "In reply to acknowledgment of receipt of the 4th edition of The Practice."

Camac next received a holographic letter from Osler which he thought so highly of that he had it framed with a photograph of Osler and hung in his study. Camac included a copy of it in his Osler correspondence. Cushing included it in his biography and noted that it was written in early March, 1902, although the letter was not dated. It follows:

1 West Franklin St., Baltimore

Dear Camac: So sorry to have missed you—will try to give you warning next time. When are you coming down? There are many things I wish to talk about with you and some of my new old treasures would delight you. Hunter McGuire[23] left me a set of Jenner's vaccination monographs—all autograph copies to his friend Shrapnell[24]—it is really a great treasure. You remember Flexner's Streptothrix case—do you not—we thought it ordinary T.B. Mrs. O. & Ike are well. So glad to hear you are getting consultations. Get out 2 or 3 good papers each year—they help.

Yours in haste, W. Osler

Cushing, in reprinting the letter, omitted the reference to Flexner's Streptothrix case.

A typewritten thank-you note, adding a friendly suggestion for an interesting investigation, follows four months later. It incorporates a statement that is surprising in view of Osler's close association with medical libraries and librarians and his influential status.

No. 1 W. Franklin Street, Baltimore
April 1st, 1902

Dear Camac: Thanks for the book, which I know I shall read with great interest.

Would it not be worth while for you to write up the question of Rush's[25] relation to Washington? By this time you could probably get access to the letters in the Philadelphia Library. They would not allow me to see them some years ago. I think it would be very interesting. Do get at it.

Love to Mrs. Camac & the baby.

Sincerely yours, W. Osler

The summer saw no letters to Camac from Osler. In the late spring he had a rather bad "Schnupfen," as he called it. Camac obviously commiserated in a letter. Because of this cold and the failing health of his 96-year-old mother the Oslers decided to forego a summer trip to England and to spend fourteen weeks at their favorite vacation spot, Pointe-à-pic, Murray Bay, on the St. Lawrence River. Osler also knew this would give him more time to prepare two addresses that were promised. One of these was "Chauvinism in Medicine."[26] Cushing points out that the obvious precision of the address was made possible by the long, unhurried summer vacation. He also began work on his Beaumont address,[27] later given in St. Louis.

Camac visited the Oslers during the summer at Murray Bay, as Osler's next letter at the end of September shows.

No. 1 W. Franklin Street, Baltimore
Sept. 30th, 1902

Dear Camac:—Glad to have your note. My cold is all gone, & I am in very good condition. I will try to send you before long a copy of a circular letter about our meeting.

We enjoyed your visit at Murray Bay very much. Do not

forget that I have an engagement with you at Mrs. Lockwood's to have a cup of tea.

Love to all at home.

Sincerely yours, W. Osler

The cryptic references to a meeting and to Mrs. Lockwood are not identifiable with certainty.

Osler's thoughtfulness for all of his students and friends is exemplified in the following letter responding to a letter of thanks from Camac.

No. 1 W. Franklin Street, Baltimore
Oct. 28th, 1902

Dear Camac: Yes, it is the Manor House at Wynford Eagle, Dorset.*

I have not heard definitely from those men as to when I am to be in New York. I will let you know.

Sincerely yours, W. Osler

Camac's note stated: *"Refers to Sydenham's birthplace a photograph of which he had sent me."

The next, a month later, expresses again Osler's interest in and concern about friends and students. He was promoting a portrait of his colleague "Popsy" Welch and hurrying back to Baltimore because of the illness of a trainee. The following day Walter Reed was to die of appendicitis and two days later H. W. Ochsner, one of Osler's internes, was to die of typhoid fever, the disease that Osler dreaded and hated the most. The young man's beloved mentor was holding his hand when he died. The letter to Camac expresses Osler's sincere concern; a note in his Commonplace book written just after Ochsner's death expresses the true depth of Osler's feeling.[28]

No. 1 W. Franklin Street, Baltimore
Nov. 21st, 1902

Dear Camac: Find out for how much Doring would paint a good portrait of Welch.

I was in New York yesterday, only for two hours, a hurried consultation. Sorry I could not see you. I had to come back at once, as poor Ochsner, one of my internes, is desperately ill with typhoid.

Love to Mrs. Camac & the baby.

Sincerely yours, W. Osler

In pursuit of the matter of a Welch portrait, another typewritten letter followed within the week.

No. 1 W. Franklin Street, Baltimore
Nov. 26, 1902

Dear Camac: Have you seen any of Doring's work, or where could I see it when I am in New York early in December? Five hundred dollars seems a very reasonable rate, and if he really is a good artist he might perhaps get some others to do here.

So glad you have seen Mr. Weir. He is a very good fellow. Give him my regards. I think it is very satisfactory the way he has progressed. Do tell him for me to go slow.

Lafleur's address is 58 University St., Montreal.

Sincerely yours, W. Osler

The next note, handwritten on his personal notepaper, from 1 West Franklin St., asks a favor but also indicates that Osler was thinking of reciprocating.

XII-1-02

Dear Camac: Will you please send word to Dr. McPhedran (Prof.Med., Toronto) at Park Ave. Hotel where & when you could show him the Clin. Laboratory at Cornell.

Yours, W. O.

P.S. Have you a copy of the Gold Headed Cane? Love to the Girls!

Later in December Osler again was helping another international friend through Camac.

> *No. 1 W. Franklin Street, Baltimore*
> *Dec. 31st, 1902*

Dear Camac: Dr. Munch[29] whose card I enclose, will be in New York on Thursday. He is out here in the interests of one of the French Journals, inspecting medical institutions. He is a very nice fellow. I have put him up at the University Club. Do you know of any place where he could get a room near by the Club? Please show him Cornell.

> *Sincerely yours, W. Osler*

Camac's response is included in the correspondence.

> *Jan. 3, 1903*
> *108 E. 65th St., N. Y. City*

My dear Doctor Osler: I have met Doctor Munch. He is dining with us tonight. I hope to have him at Cornell on Mon. He seems a nice fellow, and I am very glad you gave me the opportunity of meeting him.

Happy New Year to you.

> *Very Sincerely, C. N. B. Camac*

W. S. Thayer had also written Camac in Munch's behalf, referring to him as a "rara avis" who had come to study the institutions of the United States for a year. The letter must have been written in the early morning or late at night because Thayer closed, "With a happy New Year to you all — in which Mrs. Thayer would join me if she were yet awake."

A short time later Osler and Camac were continuing their correspondence relative to the Welch portrait. Osler wrote:

1 W. Franklin Street, Baltimore
Jan. 7th, 1903

Dear Camac: I am very much pleased with the picture. It might be a very good thing to get that man to come. He might perhaps paint Welch and me. When he has finished Mrs. Camac's picture I should like very much to see it. Do you want the photograph back?

Sincerely yours, W. Osler

Five days later, Osler was both using Camac and offering him an opportunity to enhance himself by participating in a series of Postgraduate Lectures.

No. 1 W. Franklin Street, Baltimore
Jan. 12th, 1903

Dear Camac: We have a set of evening lectures for Post-Graduates in May & June, one a week. We are asking a few of our old friends to come back & help us with these. Could you give one of them? Any subject you wish. The present aspect of the Schott treatment might be a good thing. Give a nice practical lecture that you could publish. Please let me know as soon as possible. There is not much of a fee, but there would be twenty-five dollars to pay your travelling expenses.

With love to Mrs. Camac and the baby.

Sincerely yours, W. Osler

Camac noted, "Subject: Clinical Aspects of Myocarditis!"* Camac accepted with alacrity, as his response indicates.

Jan. 13th, '03
108 E. 65th St., New York City

My Dear Dr. Osler: I would indeed be very glad of the opportunity to give one of the Post Graduate Lectures in

*Historic outline of cardiac pathology and clinical aspects of chronic myocarditis. Bulletin of the Johns Hopkins Hospital, 15: 27-38, 1904.

May or June. As to the subject, may I consider a little longer before settling it? Were I to follow your suggestion of the Schott treatment would there be any objection to broadening the topic to the treatment of heart cases? I appreciate so much your giving me this opportunity. I am so glad you like Doring's photograph. He has just gotten two more orders in New York. With love from us all, I am

Very sincerely, C. N. B. Camac

The postal service was prompt. Two days later came Osler's response from Baltimore:

No. 1 W. Franklin Street, Baltimore
Jan. 15, 1903

Dear Camac: No hurry about the title of the lecture, but you had better say you would like an early date, so that you can come in May. I hope to be in New York one day next week and shall call.

Sincerely yours, W. Osler

Osler was still toying with the idea of a portrait of himself and of Dr. Welch by Doring as the closing paragraph of Camac's response on Jan. 20th, 1903 to a letter not included in the collection attests:

Allow a little time to see the portrait, so that you can judge of Doring's capability to paint you and Doctor Welch's portrait.

Can you lunch or dine with us en famille?

The day after Camac's letter with the invitation to dine, a handwritten note from Osler arrived on his 3½ by 4½ inch card. It read:

1 W. Franklin St., Baltimore
1-21-03

Dear Camac: As I telegraphed you I could see Col. Weir with you about 4 p.m. I get to 232nd St. at 3:15. Send me word to the Club where to join you. I cannot stop with you [for] dinner as I have an engagement.

Sincerely yours, Wm. Osler

During a busy summer abroad no letters were written by Osler to Camac. It was during this summer of 1903 in Paris, that the Vernon Plaque of Osler was made.

The Oslers were nevertheless in Camac's mind as they returned from abroad. Mrs. Osler's letter of Sept. 28th, 1903, from Toronto attests to this thoughtfulness (Fig. 6).

Dear Dr. Camac: I am ashamed that I should have allowed a week to pass without writing to thank you for the lovely roses—And to convey a message of thanks left by Miss Woolley.[30] I have been doing up Dr. Oslers relatives ever since I arrived and am nearly used up—The roses came with me to Toronto and were on Mrs. Osler's table two days for her enjoyment. I hope you are feeling the benefits of your holiday. It was a pleasure having you with us and I hope you will forget the inconveniences of being turned out of sheets & towels so early. I sunned myself in my husband's glory in Montreal & as he departed at dawn Thursday not waiting to hear what was said of his address. I was inflated with pride and left very humble minded and impressed with my utter inability to cope with my position as spouse to such an adored object —

Cordially, Grace R. Osler

There is another letter from Mrs. Osler which is undated but which Camac has marked "1903." In it she wishes that they were all back at Murray Bay since "these wonderful days should not be spent in town." She goes on to twit Camac about some enigmatic activity. She writes, "Have you told your wife the truth about your behavior at M. B.? It looks rather mysterious that Dr. Osler goes so often to New York, and meets you—I suppose you three golf together." She closes with, "My love to the unseen bride."

During the Fall of 1903 Osler wrote Camac two letters that he failed to date, as was often the case. They followed Osler's presentation of his paper, "The Master Word in Medicine,"[31] at Toronto on June 29. Osler had spent part of the summer abroad "sweating out" this fine address. The first handwritten note follows:

> *University Club, Fifth Ave. & 54th St.*
> *Friday Eve. 1903*

Dear Camac: Could you come to the Club anytime before 10 AM tomorrow? I would come over to see Mrs. Camac & the new bairn but I have an engagement a few minutes after 9. Do not mind if you have any fixed engagement.

> *Sincerely yours, W. Osler*

The second letter, written two days later, reflects an error in addressing the first.

> *1 West Franklin St., Baltimore*
> *Sunday [1903]*

Dear Camac: I sent you a letter on Fri. Eve asking you to come to the Club on Sat. morning for a brief chat. I fear that I sent the letter to 64th St. I could not come around, as I had another meeting & had to leave at 10:30. I do not think I have a copy left of the Chauvinism paper. I will ask Miss H. to look it up. I hope she has sent you the Toronto address—The Master Word in Medicine.

I want to have all the old Hopkins men at dinner one night at the Club before long—what Eve. is the least likely to be preempted.

Yours Ever, W. O.

The continued interest of Osler in the welfare of his trainees is again exemplified.

A typed letter on office stationery, dated October 15th, 1903, dealt mostly with personal matters.

No. 1 Franklin Street, West, Baltimore
Oct. 15th, 1903

Dear Camac: Glad you like the little Stevenson. I was in New York last Sunday, passing through from Montreal, but I had to hurry and catch a train. I have been very much driven since I got home.

I saw the Sticineys in Paris. They are wonderfully better, both of them, and I hear from the Conynghams[32] that they have been in splendid condition. They are out in the country. They spoke of you on several occasions, and I think they quite regard you as their physician. We will go up and call there together some time. He is a decent old chap.

Glad to hear of your plan of teaching, which I am sure will prove satisfactory.

Mrs. Osler has not been at all well. She has had a recurrence of her asthmatic wheezing following the whooping-cough.[33] I have given her your letter to read. I shall hope to see you before long.

Yes, I think Savill's is a very good book. He is a nice, good fellow, and has done some excellent work in London.

Love to Mrs. Camac and the baby.

Sincerely yours, W. Osler

P.S. My consultation fee in New York is $500.

Camac pencilled a notation next to the interesting postscript which refers to Osler's consultation fee in New York: "In answer to question from me to answer patient's inquiry."

A short time later Osler wrote briefly about a subject of current interest, abdominal aortic aneurysm.

> *1 West Franklin Street, Baltimore, Md.*
> *Nov. 17th, 1903*

Dear Camac: I do hope Warren will call and see me. We are particularly interested in aneurysms just at present, as we have a group of five cases in the Wards, and I am trying to get at the question of aneurysms of the abdominal aorta, on which I have had a paper on the stocks for several years.

> *Sincerely yours, W. Osler*

Just afterward a brief letter expressed Osler's sincere regret at having to miss Camac's lecture.

> *1 West Franklin Street, Baltimore, Md.*
> *Nov. 27th, 1903*

Dear Camac: I am so sorry to hear that your lecture is to be on Dec. 1st. I have to be in New York that evening. It would have been a great pleasure to have been present at your lecture, and at the reception by McClellan.[34] I think you have chosen a very good subject.

> *Sincerely yours, W. Osler*

Another note a week later alludes to his and Mrs. Osler's chronic or recurrent respiratory problems.

> *1 West Franklin Street, Baltimore, Md.*
> *Dec. 5th, 1903*

Dear Camac: Mrs. Osler is better. She has not had any asthma for a long time now.

I heard in Philadelphia that your lecture was very good. I hope to see you before long in New York. I was disappointed that I could not go over to Janeway's[35] dinner, but I was laid up with a schnupfen for a day.

By the way, have you a copy of Friend's (*sic*) History of Medicine?[36]

With love to the family all,

Sincerely yours, W. Osler

Just before Christmas the last communication of the year was sent, a note deploring the failure of his Christmas gift to Camac to have arrived in time to send before the holiday.

1 West Franklin St.
Dec. 1903

Dear C. Thanks for the Shackford letter—most interesting. I hope Mr. Weir keeps well—give him my regards. Sorry the Gold Headed Cane[37] has not come in time to send for Xmas.

Love to all at home.

Merry Xmas.

Yours, W.O.

Early in the new year Osler was again corresponding. It sounds as though he had forgotten his reference to the *Gold Headed Cane* in his previous letter.

1 West Franklin Street, Baltimore, Md.
Jan. 2nd, 1904

Dear Camac: A Happy New Year to you!

I knew you would like Friend (*sic*). It is really one of the very best books of the kind in the literature. Have you got the Gold Headed Cane? If not I must look up a copy for you.

About Weir; I should not think it would be any special

risk for him to go south. I cannot see any special reason against it. It would probably do him a great deal of good.

If you see Mrs. Stickney before long give her my very kind regards. I am very glad you went with them to Concord.

Sincerely yours, W. Osler (Fig. 7)

Mrs. Conyngham writes to Mrs. Osler saying what a comfort you have been to them all.

In March Osler was offering help to Camac in getting a membership in the New York University Club and inviting the Camacs to come to Baltimore for a few days visit with them.

> *1 West Franklin Street, Baltimore, Md.*
> *March 3rd, 1904*

Dear Camac: I shall write to the Committee[38] at once.

I wish I could have seen more of you & Mrs. Camac & those two sweet kids. Do get Mrs. Camac to come with you & stay a few days with us this Spring. It would be delightful to have you.

Ever Yours, W. Osler

In May there came another brief typewritten letter.

> *1 West Franklin Street, Baltimore, Md.*
> *May 17th, 1904*

Dear Camac: I was awfully sorry that you had to go off so hurriedly. It was very nice indeed to see you.

Our fathers seem to have lived on Van Swieten's Commentaries. I do not remember that exact quotation of John Locke's. It is very interesting. I know one quite similar to it in spirit.

I have just finished my Harvard Lecture,[39] and shall send it to you of course as soon as it is printed.

With love to the three girls.

Sincerely yours, W. Osler

In early June Mrs. Osler was writing. Her letters, such as the one previously included, emphasize Cushing's statement that a sharper and different picture of Osler might be painted if more of her letters could be recovered.

[No date]

Dear Dr. Camac: I have just come from Canada and find your nice note with its goodly contents. You are so thoughtful. The $5 shall go towards extras on a hot day for the Tuberculosis Nurses and every penny will be appreciated. Revere sends many thanks for The Stamps. He added largely to his collection in Canada. We were so sorry your visit was cut short. You know of course there is always a bed for you and a cordial welcome.

Revere and I start north on Saturday—Miss N- follows and Dr. Osler joins us July 1st after picking up an LLD at Harvard—![40] The Immortality Lecture[41] was a great success —

Cordially Yours & gratefully

Grace R. Osler

In July, 1904, after having received information that he was being considered for the Regius Professorship of Physic at Oxford and having broken the news to Mrs. Osler, Osler handwrote Camac, on the verge of his departure for England, without mentioning the subject.

VII-10-04
Pointe-à-Pic, P.Q.

Dear Camac: So sorry to hear from Bowditch[42] that your sweet Lassie was ill—I hope she is all right now. Not having heard again he said he thought all was going smoothly. I shall be in N.Y. on Friday next before sailing

& will look you up. I wish you were here—'tis a delightful spot.

Love to Mrs. Camac.

Sincerely yours, Wm. Osler

Immediately following his return from his brief visit to England Osler wrote Camac, along with many others, of his decision, ten days earlier, to accept the proffered Regius Professorship. Camac has marked this letter "Important." It was forwarded to Camac in Nova Scotia where he was vacationing. It was written on New York University Club stationery and was dated the "14th" [August, 1904].

Dear Camac: I have just come from your house—sorry not to find you at home, tho' glad that you are away for a good rest, I hope.

I had much to talk about with you. I have taken a serious step—I leave Baltimore next year; after the session. I have accepted the Chair of Medicine at Oxford. Virtually it is a retirement as there is no Clinical School but a purely Academic berth. With as little or as much teaching as one likes. I am tired of the strain of the past few years which could have only one end—a break down. I have had less & less time for my clinical work & it is not very soul inspiring to have a daily grind of practice & growing worse year by year. Oxford is a delightful place—sweet and peaceful & Sanderson[43] whom I succeed is my old teacher & friend. I shall miss a great deal—particularly the association with my old boys in Baltimore & elsewhere. I had intended to quit in 1909 if I lasted so long so this only cuts off four years—four doubtful ones at the present pace.

I hope you are all right—& that Mrs. Camac & the bairns are well.

Sincerely yours, Wm. Osler (Fig. 8)

Mrs. Osler's reaction to the news is of interest and expressed well in a letter written after Osler had rejoined her at their vacation spot on the St. Lawrence, at Murray Bay, at the end of August or first of September.

Pointe-à-Pic
Sunday Eve. [No date]

Dear Dr. Camac: I have a feeling that I should like to put my arms around about six or eight of *our very own* men and hug them hard—needless to say you would be a victim to this impulse. All that you and the others express for Dr. Osler—all you say of his influence etc. touches me deeply. And during these days of diversified feelings I hardly know how to express my appreciation and sympathy & you can never know what a struggle it has been and such hard work for me to encourage Dr. Osler to do what I knew was really the best for him—I am sure he can never regret this—but we both anticipate woeful days —I hope you are having a good rest and outing. I have been here peacefully since June 29th. In the early summer I heard very regretfully of the anxieties that beset you and Mrs. Camac about the children. I trust all is well now with them. Dr. Osler is looking very well and really having a holiday except for stacks of mail. We leave here the 14th [September] for Toronto[44] spending the 15th in Montreal. I am going to Toronto while Dr. Osler is [in] St. Louis[45]—and then to the Conynghams I think. We do not break camp [for Oxford] until next May and hope to see you in Baltimore before that. Your cousins-in-law here are all well—

Bestest regards & love to you both.

Yours Cordially, Grace R. Osler

Norman Gwyn[46] is here & both McCraes have just left.

A note pencilled by Mrs. Osler on her card with an accompanying envelope stamped "Waldorf-Astoria, Oct. 18, 6:08 pm, 1904, New York" carries a provocative message. It says, "I am awfully sorry but I am just in a tub. I am going to Boston tomorrow at 10. Missed you dreadfully at M.B. [Murray Bay].   G.R.O"

A note in pencil on the back of a calling card of "The Regius Professor of Medicine; Oxford," states simply, "Sorry I have only an hour. We go on by the 1 o'clock train to Boston. Yours, W.O." On the face of the card where Osler had pencilled out the "Regius Professor" Camac wrote the date, "Dec. 24, 1904" and the following note; "Left at my house as he was leaving for Europe to take up his new duties at Oxford as The Regius Professor of Medicine. I saw them at Grand Central Station. Was with arsenic poisoning case when he called. He had been in Oxford the summer previous." Camac must have written this note many years later. Actually, the Oslers were on their way to Jamaica Plain to spend Christmas with Mrs. Osler's sister.[47] They went from there to Toronto to visit Osler's mother. They were not due to depart for Oxford for over four months.

The next note from Osler was handwritten on 1, West Franklin Street stationery and dated only "1st." Although Camac later marked this 1904 it seems to have been written January 1, 1905.

Dear Camac: Happy New Year to you & the family. I am so glad you liked the Volume. I like the idea for the quotation(?) calendar very much—Would it be possible to get enough good things to fill in? I doubt it. I hope to

Figure 1. Lieutenant Colonel, C. N. B. Camac in military uniform during World War I.

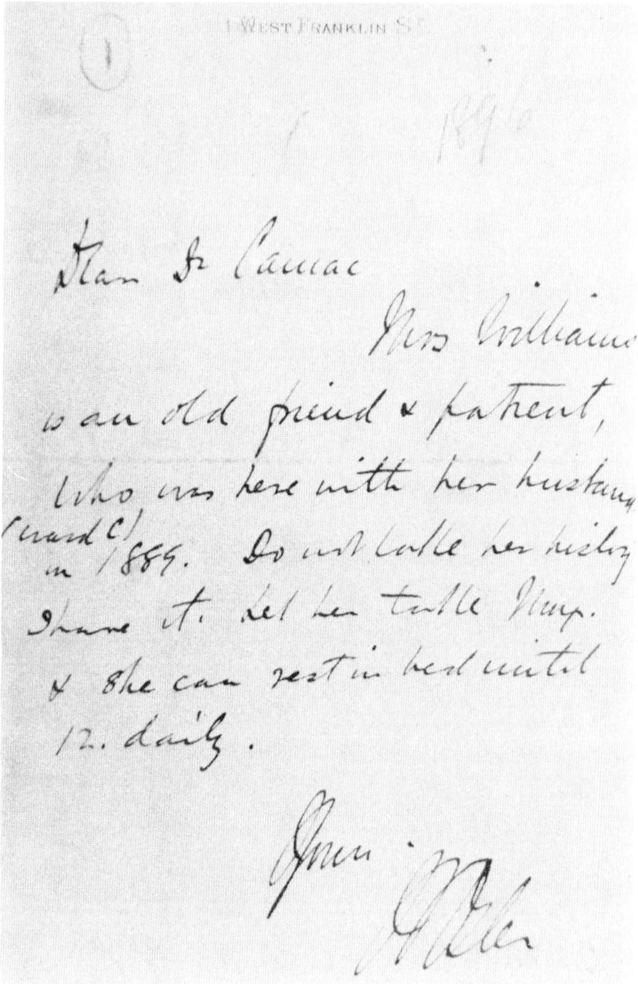

1 West Franklin St.

1890

Dear Dr Camac

Mrs Williams is an old friend & patient, who was here with her husband (ward C) in 1889. Do not take her history I have it. Let her take Mag. & she can rest in bed until 12. daily.

Yours W Osler

Figure 2. First letter from Osler to Camac.

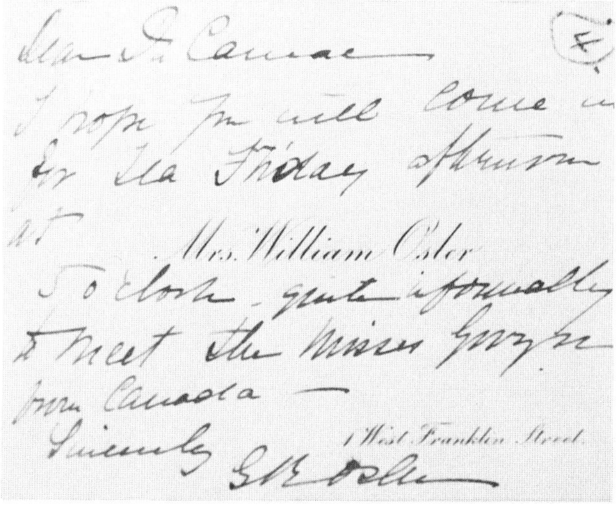

Dear Dr. Camac—
I hope you will come in for tea Friday afternoon at
Mrs. William Osler
5 o'clock quite informally to meet the Misses Gwyn from Canada—
Sincerely
1 West Franklin Street.
G. R. Osler

Figure 3. First note from Mrs. Osler to Camac.

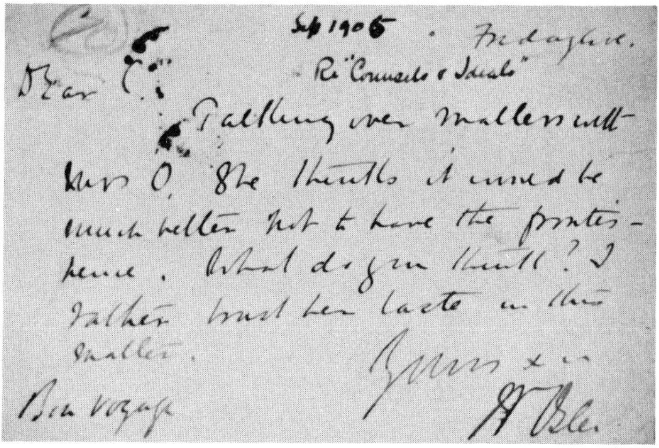

Sep 1905. Friday
Re "Counsels & Ideals"
Dear C.
Talking over matters with Mrs O. She thinks it would be much better not to have the frontispiece. What do you think? I rather trust her taste in this matter.
Yours ever
W Osler
Bon voyage

Figure 10. Card from Osler relating to the frontispiece for the first edition of *Counsels and Ideals.*

Figure 4. Photograph of Osler taken in Toronto in 1896,
the year Camac started with him.

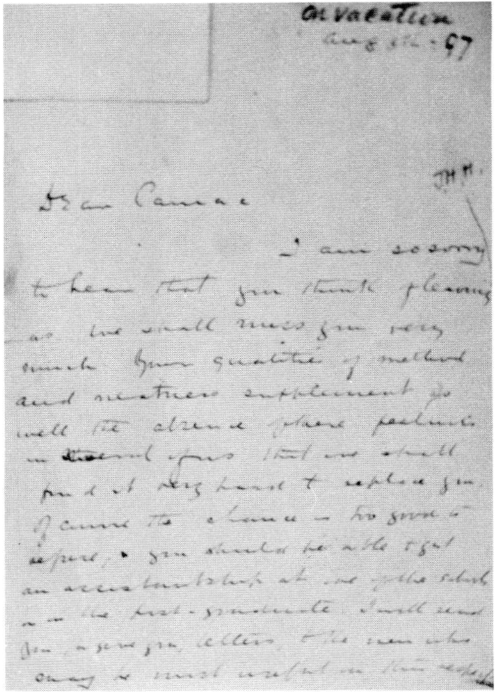

Figure 5. Letter from Osler to Camac concerning Camac's departure from Johns Hopkins.

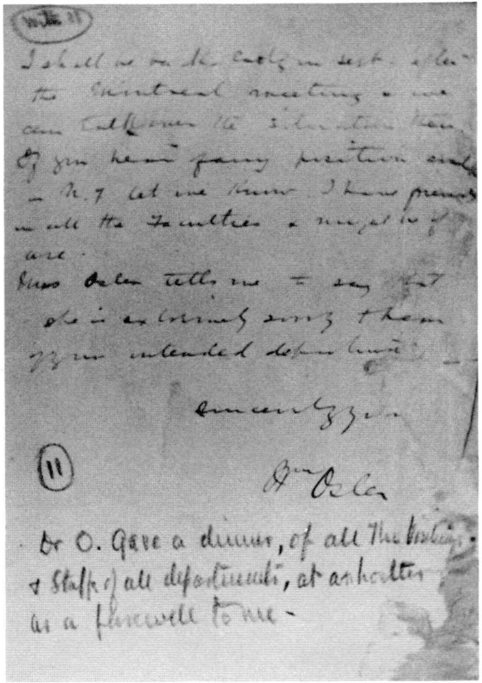

Figure 6. Photograph of Mrs. Osler taken in 1904.

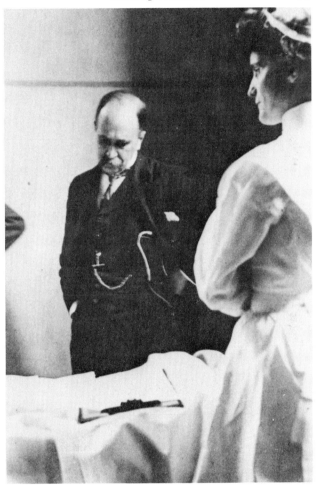

Figure 7. Osler, "The Chief," at patient's bedside at Johns Hopkins about 1904.

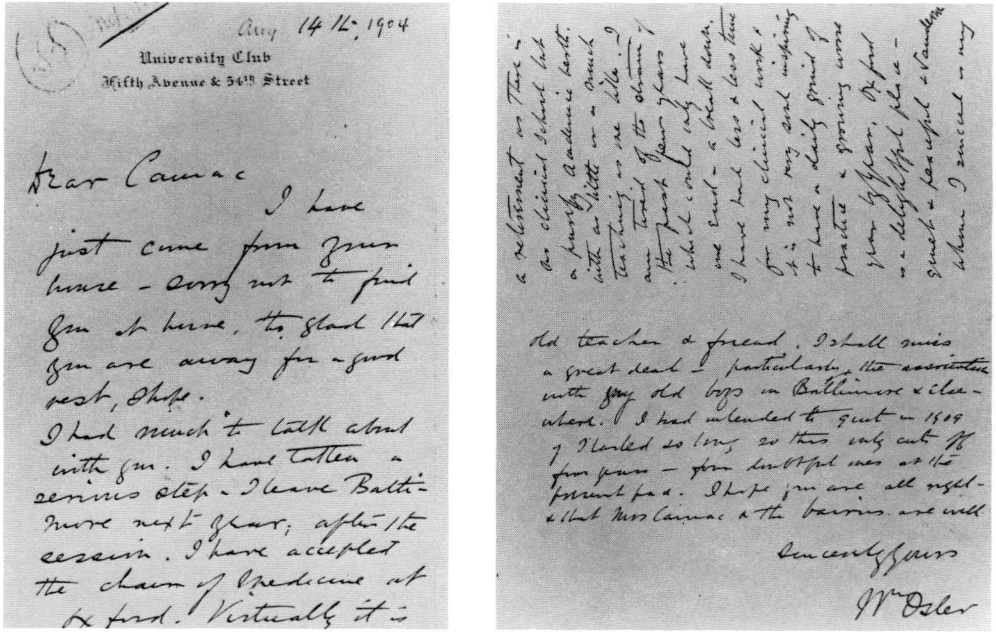

Figure 8. Letter of August 14, 1904 informing Camac of Osler's decision to leave Johns Hopkins for Oxford.

Figure 9. Snapshot of Oslers in garden at Oxford, June 1905.
Dr. W. W. Francis wrote that Osler's glum expression was related
to the recent move.

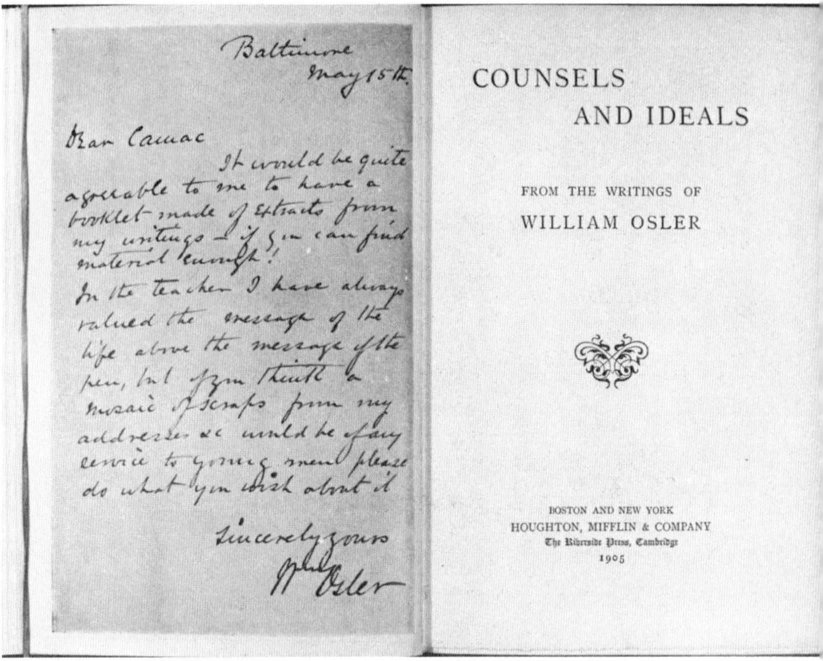

Baltimore
May 15th

Dear Camac

It would be quite agreeable to me to have a booklet made of extracts from my writings — if you can find material enough!! In the teacher I have always valued the message of the life above the message of the pen, but if you think a mosaic of scraps from my addresses &c would be of any service to young men please do what you wish about it

Sincerely yours

Wm Osler

COUNSELS
AND IDEALS

FROM THE WRITINGS OF
WILLIAM OSLER

BOSTON AND NEW YORK
HOUGHTON, MIFFLIN & COMPANY
The Riverside Press, Cambridge
1905

Figure 11. Title page and frontispiece of first edition of
Counsels and Ideals.

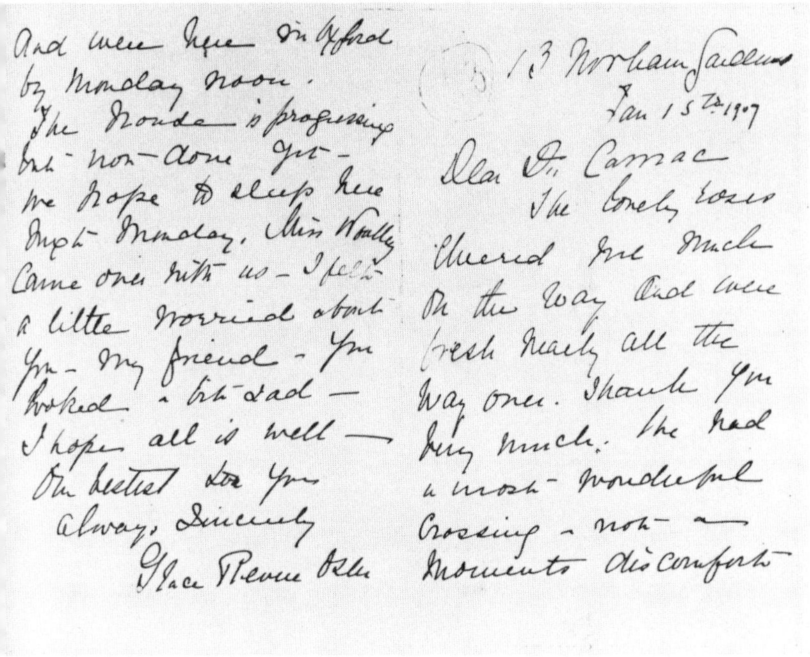

And were here in Oxford
by Monday noon.
The House is progressing
but now done yet—
We hope to sleep here
Supt Monday. Miss Woolley
came over with us—I felt
a little worried about
you—my friend—You
looked a bit sad—
I hope all is well—
Our bestest love you
always, sincerely
Grace Revere Osler

13 Norham Gardens
Jan 15th 1907
Dear Dr. Camac
The lovely roses
cheered me much
on the way and were
fresh nearly all the
way over. Thank you
very much. We had
a most wonderful
crossing—not a
moments discomfort—

Figure 12. Letter from Mrs. Osler to Camac following
Osler's mother's centenary celebration.

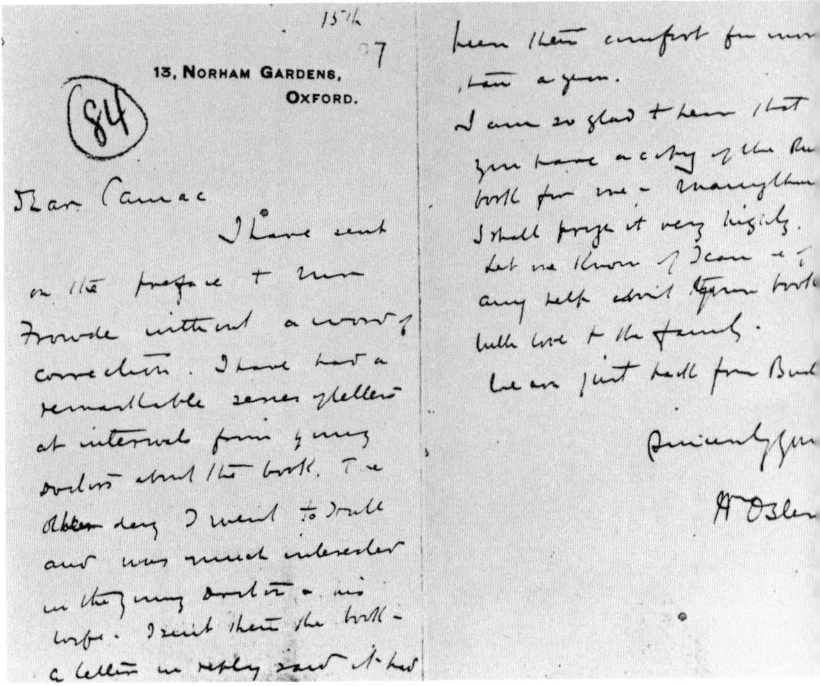

Figure 13. Osler's first letter to Camac on the stationery of their new home at 13 Norham Gardens, "The Open Arms."

Figure 14. Photograph of Osler dated by him, Nov. 20, 1912.

From the Regius Professor of Medicine, Oxford.

29th Jan. 1913.

Dear Camac,

It was very nice to get your letter this mroning, and last evening the report on the Ottawa typhoid, which is most interesting.

I am so glad to hear that Mrs. Camac is better. What a sad time she has had'. I shall get out in time for the meeting on the 16th of April, and a day or two before that you may expect a telephone call, and I shall of course run round and see you at once. Give my love to the girls and say that I am sorry· I have had to stop all business relations with their firm, because of the sand in the sugar. I hope the opening of the new milinery department will be ready by the time I get out. Revere is very well. He has left Winchester this term to have a year's tutoring in Latin and Greek, in which he is weak, for his entrance examination.

With love to you all,.

Sincerely yours,

Figure 15. Example of typewritten letter from Osler on letterhead of the Regius Professor of Medicine. It contains references to the children of each.

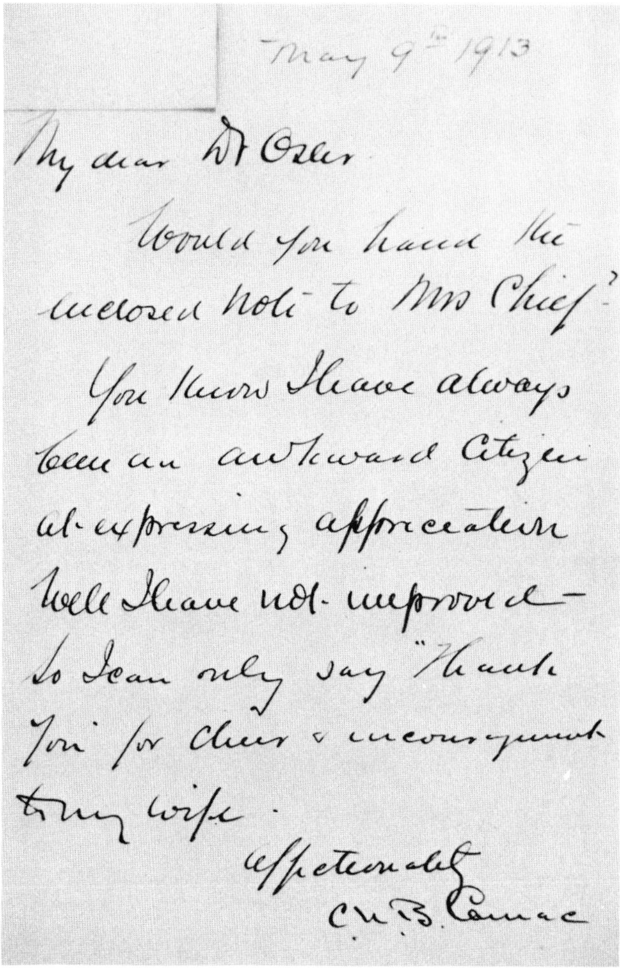

May 9ᵗʰ 1913

My dear Dr Osler

Would you hand the
enclosed note to Mrs Chief?

You know I have always
been an awkward citizen
at expressing appreciation
Well I have not improved —
So I can only say "thank
You" for cheer & encouragement
to my wife.
Affectionately
C.N.B. Camac

Figure 16. Letter from Camac to Osler which accompanied gift to
Lady Osler from proceeds of sale of *Counsels and Ideals* with
which she was to purchase a gift for Osler.

Figure 17. Osler (center) with some of the staff at the American Woman's Hospital, Paignton, England, 1915. The man seated at Osler's left is thought to be Camac.

see you this week in N.Y. I have a consultation Wednesday or Thursday. I will let you know. Mrs. Osler sends love—

Yours Ever, W. O.

Shortly thereafter Osler's secretary, Miss Humpton, wrote Camac again about the elusive *Gold Headed Cane*. This was on Osler's professional letterhead.

No. 1 Franklin Street, West, Baltimore
Jan. 4th, 1905

Dear Dr. Camac: I have my eye on a copy of the Gold-Headed Cane for you, and I write to make sure that you have not received a copy from Dr. Osler since you spoke of it to me. If you will let me know, I shall send you the copy at once.

Happy New Year.

Sincerely Yours, Olean Humpton

Osler's next letter relates to a newspaper clipping sent to him by Camac, concerning "The Fixed Period" Address[48] which had been delivered on February 22, 1905.

1, West Franklin St., Baltimore, Md.
April 5th, 1905

Dear Camac: Many thanks for your clipping. There is always sure to be a reaction, & meanwhile I have been quite content, feeling that, at least, my friends have appreciated my point of view. Mrs. Osler will be stopping with the Conynghams at the Waldorf on Saturday on her way north to say good-bye to my mother. She said a few minutes ago that she would try to see you and Mrs. Camac.

Sincerely Yours, Wm. Osler

Camac appended the following note to this letter. "After the address on old age which caused so much discussion of nature unpleasant and trying to Dr. Osler."

As the Oslers prepared to leave for Oxford Miss B. O. Humpton, Osler's secretary, wrote Camac again, this time in response to an inquiry from Camac about completing his collection of Osler reprints. The letter is included in the correspondence.

No. 1 Franklin Street, West, Baltimore
May 9th, 1905

Dear Dr. Camac: I am very sorry, but the reprints had to be shipped off to the hospital, and I had not a moment to go over them. I have sent your list to Miss Blogg,[49] the Librarian, and have asked her, when she arranges them, to send to you any that are on your list.

Very truly yours, B.O. Humpton

P.S. I enclose a list of the papers which have appeared since the binding of the last set. I have forgotten just how far your set goes, so they may overlap. The most of these Miss Blogg can send you.

Early Oxford Days

1905-1911

CAMAC had been considering for some time the preparation of a collection of extracts from Osler's addresses and publications. Soon after the Oslers departed for Oxford he was to follow in order to pursue the project near Dr. Osler, his mentor. The first of Osler's letters to Camac that seems to relate to this project was written from Scotland where the Oslers had gone soon after reaching England, for a vacation. It was written on the letterhead of the Station Hotel of the Highland Railway on the Kyle of Lochalsh.[50] The handwritten letter is undated but must have been written in August, 1905. It related to a publisher for the material that Camac had been busy assembling.[51]

Dear Camac: The arrangements seem most satisfactory— £100 is a very reasonable sum and if the book sells for $1.00 the sale of 1000 could cover the expenses—less the cost of importation. Lea Bros. or Appleton would probably take the American edition. Blakiston has the Osleriana and the Aequanimitas but he might like this also—he is a good fellow and would handle it well; what do you say to asking him first? Saunders would scarcely [undecipherable] it as he prints his own books.[52] I will look over the whole stuff carefully & have it read by someone selected by Mr. Hart. I will send you [undecipherable] before you leave. We shall return to Oxford about the 5th I think. We shall have had enough of the heather in the next ten days. You could come down and talk over the final arrangements. It has been a great pleasure to see you.

Yours Ever, W. O.

Osler's first letter to Camac from Oxford was dated the "6th. Just back." It had to be September, 1905. It follows:

> 7 *Norham Gardens, Oxford*
> *6th. Just back.*

Dear Camac: Come when ever you can—& come directly to us. We had a delightful visit in Scotland. I found the parcel on my table & will get at it this Eve.

Yours Ever, W. O.

The parcel referred to was material for Camac's *Counsels and Ideals from the Writings of William Osler*, which Camac had been working on during the summer in Oxford.

Osler wrote another correspondent that his mind was rather "dessicated" at this time and Cushing attributes the scarcity of correspondence during this period to this fact (Fig. 9).

Most of the correspondence this first summer in England came from Mrs. Osler. As Cushing suggested, it gives a different insight into Osler as well as a better understanding of his helpmate. Like so many of her letters they bear no date. Camac notes that each was received during the summer of 1905. The scolding first letter perhaps demonstrates even better than the second one Mrs. Osler's true affection for Camac.

7 *Norham Gardens, Oxford*
Saturday p.m.

[no salutation] Very nice about the baby—but very horrid that you missed going with us to Ewelme—but you are such a D — g that I don't care really—I am very cross with you about not coming back here. Dr. Parsons is here and *likes to stay here.* You better spend tomorrow here or I shall be raging. Dinner at 1:30 — Tea 4:30 — Supper 8 P.M.

Yours, G. R. Osler

Tuesday
*Beaufort Castle,*53 *Beauly, N. B.*
[Embossed]

Dear Dr. Camac: We are leaving here this afternoon for Skye.54 Dr. Osler will write you from there. We have a most glorious week & only occasional showers. Revere has fished to his heart's content but with not much luck. Dr. Osler is looking brown & robust. It has been a splendid outing for him—we had one day on the moors on Loch Ness with most wonderful views—we have motored in all directions—There have only been a few guests in the house and we have had much independence which you know I consider real hospitality. I hope you made use of the carriage or of 7 Norham Gardens in some way. It has been such a pleasure having you with us—and I hope it is one we may often look forward to—our love to you.

Affectionately, Grace R. Osler

This was the time during which Camac was working on *Counsels and Ideals.* Dr. Osler even commiserated with Mrs. Camac about Dr. Camac's absence from her and the diligence with which he was working. Camac was in England from June into September.

The Oslers returned from Scotland the first week of September.

7 Norham Gardens, Oxford
Sept. 1st, 1905

Dear Mrs. Camac—I am so sorry to think that you have been in seclusion for the summer. I wish you had been over here with C.B.N. [*sic*]. We have enjoyed having him so much, and he has worked so much. I never saw him in such good condition. I am sure he is fit to take up his work for the winter with renewed vigor. I hope you will be able to join him before long. Drop me a line to say how you are. You will be so pleased with Charles little book—I am surprised to find how much he has gathered from my scraps and tags of addresses. With best wishes.

Sincerely Yours, Wm. Osler

About this time[55] Camac received an interesting letter from Amy Gwyn[56] and this is included in the correspondence. Camac wrote on the letter that the verse contained in the letter "was repeated to Dr. O. and me by Mrs. O., Dr. Osler's mother, in her 99th year." He adds, "Dr. O. and I visited her just before he left U.S. for Oxford."

"Staplehurst," Dundas, Ont.
August 31st

My dear Dr. Camac: I had not forgotten my promise about sending you those verses, but not quite sure of them myself have waited to get them first hand from my mother[57] and now I think this is as Grandmother repeated

"You must send if aught should ail thee
To Willis, Hebberden and Bailey [*sic*]
All exceeding skilful men
Willis, Bailey and Hebberden!
But doubtful which most sure to kill is
Bailey, Hebberden or Willis."[58]

I am sure you must be enjoying Murray Bay after the horrible heat in Toronto last week—now we are having a decided siege of Autumn.

We heard from Oxford this morning. All well & happy is the report.

With kind rememberances to Mrs. Camac.

Very Sincerely Yours, Amy Gwyn

The visit with Osler to Osler's mother on the eve of his departure for England was the occasion when she admonished her son: "Remember, Willie, the shutters in England will rattle as they do in America."[59]

Shortly before Camac was to sail for home in September 1905 he received a handwritten postal card addressed to "Dr. C.B.N. [sic] Camac, Steamer Friederich der Grosse, North German Lloyd S.S. Co., Cherbourg, France."

Friday Eve.

Dear C. Talking over matters with Mrs. O. She thinks it would be much better not to have the frontispiece. What do you think? I rather trust her taste in this matter.

Yours, W. Osler (Fig. 10)

Bon voyage.

Camac had proposed using a portrait of Osler for a frontispiece for the book. Mrs. Osler made her point, however, and the first edition of *Counsels and Ideals* carried a letter from Osler to Camac instead of the portrait as frontispiece.

By the end of the month Osler had seen the proof and responded with enthusiasm.

Dear Camac: The *bronze it is* and not the lady! I think it
will be very good. I am leaving out the verse for the dedication to the lady, as it looks rather as if it contained a
reference to the newspaper hullabaloo about chloroform.
The proof is splendid and it really will be first class, only
I do not like not to have your name on the title page.
What do you think? Your introduction is splendid. I think
the book should have a very good sale. I will have a copy
very nicely bound for Mrs. Camac for Christmas. I hope
you found her better.

Ever Yours, Wm. Osler

I have filled in all the dates except R. L. Macdonnell[60]
[Holographic postscript]

There is no record of the verse referred to in the
letter. The dedication remained simply "To Grace
Revere Osler." Camac's name appeared on the spine
of the book but not on the title page. Camac had
asked Osler to fill in the dates of some of his publications from which excerpts were taken. Osler
evidently did not have the information relating to
his paper on R. L. MacDonnell. These references are
listed at the beginning of the book. "The bronze"
referred to in the first sentence was evidently the
Vernon Plaque commissioned by H. B. Jacobs[61] in
1903. The reference is obscure. Perhaps it was considered for the frontispiece. It appears again in a
letter from Mrs. Osler expressing her surprise and
gratitude concerning the dedication.

7, *Norham Gardens, Oxford.*
Oct. 11th [1905]

My dear Dr. Camac: I do not see how you all kept the secret of the dedication of the [book] so cleverly from me —You both seemed surrounded by mystery always and I resisted asking questions. I am really very deeply touched by your thought of dedicating the book to me—and only regret the verdict was against the verse. I am sure you will understand. Dr. Osler wrote you I suppose that we always felt that Dr. Jacobs was not quite pleased at having the bronze distributed at the Charaka dinner[62]—I did not feel that he would at all care for the general circulation. Dr. Osler had your cable and yesterday a letter from Mrs. Camac. I rejoice that she is so much better and hope you will soon have your home established in good form. We had a delightful week in Paris but to tell you the truth I do not think the English or American men took much pleasure in the Congress.[63] The opening ceremonies were very impressive and Mon. Loubet spoke most charmingly. We had Dr. Palter [?] here one day after you left & I liked him so much. American[s] continue to come but I fancy this week will see the last of them. Dr. Osler is perfectly enchanted with "Counsels & Ideals"—And speaks so often of the pleasure it is to have you do it. It always seems to me that the satisfaction of having young men devoted to Dr. Osler is doubled by his devotion to them—It was such a comfort having you here this summer. I often think our first months here would have been depressing had it not been for the western breezes so constantly blowing in —Our bestest love to you—

Your affectionate old friend, Grace Revere Osler

A month later Mrs. Osler responded joyfully upon receipt of the first copy of *Counsels and Ideals* (Fig. 11). This letter was on stationery with the family "Fidelis" crest.

Friday, Nov. 17th [1905]

My dear Dr. Camac: You would have felt fully repaid this afternoon could you have seen Dr. Osler strutting into the drawing room & handing me the first copy of "Counsels & Ideals," bound in most beautiful blue and perfect in every respect. Last evening I found him coddling it by the fire. I don't know which pleases him most—your part, the binding or the first thought of yours about doing it. Really it is charmingly done and the binding adds to the charm. I am sure you will feel perfectly satisfied & thoroughly repaid for your summers rest. I hope good health for your beloved during the winter will add to your pleasure. Yesterday I had your letter of Nov. 6th—so it was a day of general rejoicing. We continue to flourish and have had wonderful sunshine. We sail on the Coronia of the Cunard Line on Dec. 16th and hope to arrive on Sunday the 24th and make rapidly for Boston. Our love to you four—

Affectionately & gratefully, Grace Revere Osler

The following day a typed letter from Dr. Osler echoed his wife's enthusiasm.

7, Norham Gardens, Oxford.
November 18th, 1905

Dear Camac: An advance copy of the book [*Counsels & Ideals*] reached Mrs. Osler yesterday. It is splendid, and we all feel so deeply indebted to you for it. I am sure it will prove a great success. I think it should be electrotyped. There is certain to be a demand for more than fifteen hundred copies. To electrotype it now would cost very little, not a tenth of what it would be to set the type again. Mr. Hart[64] says he would keep the type up until Christmas.

I am delighted to hear that Mrs. Camac is better. I have ordered a handsomely bound copy of the little book for her.

I am glad to hear that Brannam will introduce clinical clerks in the municipal hospitals. Well arranged, it would prove the most important advance in medical education ever made in New York.

Sincerely Yours, Wm. Osler

The next handwritten note on plain stationery was written on December 28, 1905 while the Oslers were visiting in the north.

Thursday

Dear Camac: I am due in Baltimore next Friday, 5th [Jan., 1906] from Toronto. Let me know there how long Mrs. Shilling's mother is to be in N.Y. I could come in *any* day. I have just seen about Forbes death. I fear they will think McClellan a bit "aged." He certainly has earned the promotion.

Yours, W. O.

And from Baltimore came a typewritten note concerning another consultation.

Johns Hopkins Hospital, North Broadway.
Baltimore, Jan. 15th, 1906

Dear Camac: I could see Mrs. Foster with you at twelve o'clock on Wednesday. Sorry I cannot lunch with you, but I am engaged.

Sincerely Yours, W. Osler

Another brief typed note demonstrates Osler's busy schedule while visiting North America.

Johns Hopkins Hospital, North Broadway.
Baltimore, Jan. 23rd, 1906

Dear Camac: I will be in New York the day before I sail, and I hope to be able to see you. I am going to Toronto on Tuesday.[65]

Ever Yours, W. Osler

One more holographic letter was written before Osler's departure. He was still on the move.

> *Johns Hopkins Hospital, North Broadway*
> *Baltimore, Jan. 29th, 1906*

Dear Camac: Your announcement of a new impression* is most satisfactory. I am so glad the type was not distributed. Miss H.[66] says there are several misprints—she will send memo. I leave for Toronto tomorrow Eve. & return to New York Friday. I will call sometime thro the day. I doubt if I can join you at lunch or dinner. I have two people coming from Montreal to see me & I have a number of people to see. I will let you know.

Love to Mrs. Camac.

> *Yours, W. O.*

After returning to England Osler next wrote on March 16, 1906. He refers to matters raised in Camac's letters. There also is a mention of the success of *Counsels and Ideals.* The letter is typed on 7, Norham Gardens stationery (the home of Dr. & Mrs. Max Mueller which the Oslers had on loan) and Osler comments on their indecision about a permanent house, which later turned out to be next door, at 13 Norham Gardens.

> *7, Norham Gardens, Oxford.*
> *March 16th, 1906*

Dear Camac: I saw a very good review of your booklet in the Athenaeum last week. It is satisfactory that it has gone off so well. Ramsay's books are of great value. They have been frequently reprinted and they ought not to be difficult to get. He was a charming character—a versatile, many-sided man. You know about his tragic end. I have seen a good deal of Wright's work which is most interesting, and I think along the right lines.

*[Camac: "Counsels and Ideals"]

We have not yet settled on a house, but are busy making preliminaries.

Love to Mrs. Camac,

Sincerely yours, Wm. Osler

[Osler penned a postscript:] I am sending a delightful little book—also by McMichael [*sic*]—of biographies.[67]

Mrs. Osler next wrote. Her letter was filled with news of activities that were to continue to be of interest. They had taken possession of their new house just twelve days before:

> *7 Norham Gardens, Oxford*
> *August 12th [1906]*

Dear Dr. Camac: Dr. Futcher's[68] letter has made us all homesick for Murray Bay and for you—your being part of our first summer here—rather made us feel that you belonged to us—It is nice however—to think of you in a familiar spot. I hope you are not doing anything to shock the Lawrences. That is always an important matter at Caribou. I am sure you will be disappointed that Dr. Osler is not going over. I am selfishly glad. We are much involved in building—enlarging the house, No. 13—and Dr. Osler must help with his advice. Fortunately we can have this house until December and I shall hope to move the family before we sail. We must be in Toronto for Mrs. Osler's 100th birthday on December 14th. We spent two weeks at Ewelme[69]—it is perfectly delightful there now. The Master's rooms are most comfortable. The old furniture has been done up and really everything is in excellent order. It has been great fun doing it. The old men and women have cheered up. We gave a picnic while we were in residence & had 120 school children. Taking them and the old people in brakes [?] to a beautiful common about 6 miles away for tea. Dr. Osler had the safe opened and found it contained many very interesting papers—but all covered with mould. They are now being cared for and will be bound and protected. Our love to you and your dear family from us both.

Affectionately, G. R. Osler

It was six months before Osler next responded to a letter or letters from Camac. Camac was preparing a book that was to be called *Epoch-Making Contributions to Medicine, Surgery and the Allied Sciences.* Camac was seeking Osler's help in securing Lord Lister's[70] permission to have the book dedicated to him.

> 7, *Norham Gardens, Oxford.*
> *September 14th, 1906*

Dear Camac: I have sent your letter on to Lord Lister. I doubt very much if you will get any reply. I hear he is failing very much. I do not think it would be considered amiss if you went ahead without any actual consent. I am sure he would be very pleased.

We were very sorry that you did not come over. There are all sorts of things that would interest you deeply. I have just returned from Scotland, where we have spent a delightful fortnight.

I do hope Saunders will approve of the scheme. It would be well to have the title page of the *De Motu Cordis* reproduced. Of course it would not be expensive.

It was a great disappointment not to be at the Toronto meeting. I am so glad you saw my mother.

Sincerely yours, Wm. Osler

Osler's influence is manifest in a letter from Lord Lister to Camac dated September 18, 1906, just four days after Osler's letter to Camac. This handwritten letter is reproduced as the introduction to the first

chapter of Camac's book. In this chapter was reproduced Joseph Lister's paper, "On the Antiseptic
Principle of the Practice of Surgery," originally published in 1867. Saunders published Camac's book in
1909. It was dedicated to Lord Lister. Lister's respect
for Osler is expressed in his letter. In it he wrote,
"Professor Osler's recommendation removes any
hesitancy I might otherwise have felt in giving my
cordial assent to your proposal."

The second chapter deals with Harvey's work on
circulation of the blood. However, Osler's suggestion concerning reproduction of the title page of
De Motu Cordis was not followed for some reason.

The next letter, and the last one during 1906, was
written from Toronto in December. The Oslers had
arrived in New York on December 6. After a round
of receptions and dinners in Baltimore and a stop
in Hamilton[71] they arrived in Toronto the day before Dr. Osler's mother's 100th birthday.

The *New York Times* reported the upcoming
event as follows and Camac attached the clipping
to Osler's letter:

Mrs. Osler 100 Years Old.

One of Her Sons Is the Regius Professor of Medicine at
Oxford. Special to the *New York Times*. Toronto, Ontario,
Dec. 13. [1906]. Mrs. Featherson[72] [*sic*] Osler will celebrate
her one-hundredth birthday to-morrow. Her children and
grandchildren, outlying kindred and lifelong friends, have
journeyed from the four quarters of the earth to rejoice
with her in the celebration of her centenary.

Dr. William Osler, Regius Professor of Medicine in the
University of Oxford, has arrived with his wife and son.

With the members of the family and immediate connections living in Toronto, the party to-morrow will number between eighty and ninety.

Never in the history of Canada has any woman been the mother of four such distinguished men as Judge Osler of the Ontario Court of Appeals; E. B. Osler, M. P.; Dr. Osler of Oxford, and the late B. B. Osler, one of the most distinguished lawyers who every pleaded in a Canadian court.

Mrs. Osler was born in Kent, England, and came to Canada with her husband, the late Canon Osler, in 1837.

The day following the birthday, December 15, 1906, Osler wrote Camac from his brother Edmund's home:

> *Saturday*
> *Craigleigh,*[73] *Rosedale*

Dear Camac: The centenary was a great success & mother stood the fatigues of the day wonderfully. She is so bright and well and enjoyed every thing. I wish you could have seen the 28 gt. gdchildren & gt. nephews about the big cake with its 100 candles.[74] I shall see you of course when in N.Y.

> *Yours ever, Wm. Osler*

Mrs. Osler wrote next to thank Camac for roses which he presented as the Oslers were departing for England (Fig. 12).

> *13 Norham Gardens*
> *Jan. 15th [1907]*

Dear Dr. Camac: The lovely roses cheered me much on the way and were fresh nearly all the way over. Thank you very much. We had a most wonderful crossing—not a moments discomfort and were here in Oxford by Monday noon. The house is progressing but not done yet—we hope to sleep here next Monday. Miss Woolley came over with us—I felt a little worried about you—my friend—you looked a bit sad—I hope all is well—Our bestest to you.

Always Sincerely, Grace Revere Osler

After a lapse in the correspondence during the busy summer of 1907 Osler found time to write a long, interesting letter from Bude, on the north coast of Cornwall where the Oslers had gone for a vacation, in September. This was the first letter written on the new 13 Norham Gardens stationery (Fig. 13) and is dated simply "5th." The envelope is postmarked, "Bude—S.O.—Cornwall." It was addressed to Camac at Caribou Cottage, Pointe-à-Pic, where they had vacationed together in the past.

5th
13 Norham Gardens, Oxford

Dear Camac: I am so glad to hear that you have made final arrangements with Saunders.[75] Would it not be helpful to have the title-pages of some of the books reproduced —just as in my Browne article[76] by the new process—it is not expensive. The *De Motu Cordis*, Laennec 1st edition &c would add greatly to the interest of the work. You will have hard work to keep within the limits of 400 pages. I am sorry in a way that you did not come over & try the Press. Let me know if I can be of any help in getting pictures &c. What title? all important, consult Welch.[77] I knew you would like the Charaka men—Dana is a trump & it is a good group. I wish we had a club like it over here.

The Press[78] is issuing for us a new Quarterly Jr. of Med. in connection with our new assoc. of British Physicians, both hobbies of mine which I hope may stir up clinical study. I will send you a copy next month. I am delighted to hear about Harding & will write him at once. He deserves his success. We have had a very busy summer. T. McCrae, Futcher, Barker, Boggs[79] & others have been with us. McCrae has lost his heart to one of my nieces Miss Amy Gwyn. We are all delighted. Counsels & Ideals seems to keep up a good sale here. I do not think a photo would help. I would have liked that profile of the medallion by Vernon but Jacobs does not wish it reproduced. [This sentence deleted by Cushing in *The Life*.] I am trying to get my biographical essays together in a companion vol to Aequanimitas—under the title "An Alabama Student & others" &c.[80] The Press will take it.

I have given two lectures this summer in the Extension Course one on Early Medical Work in Oxford dealing with the scholastic & renaissance periods the other An Introduction to the Study of the *Anatomy of Melancholy.* The former I must still work on as part of a study of the whole subject of Oxford Med. (in 4 periods—Scholastic, Renaissance, Caroline & Victorian) the latter I have nearly ready.[81] We have got out the Burton Books at Ch. Ch.[82] I am having them all put together & am collecting all the editions to put under a copy of the Brasenose picture which will be an insert among the books. Love to Mrs. Camac & the bairns, to the McCaggs, the Bowditches— tap your rt. ventricle when you meet Margie B. for me & your left when you meet Lois S.[83] Mrs. Osler sends love.

Yours, Wm. Osler

Returning from Bude, Osler found the preface prepared by Camac for the fourth impression of *Counsels and Ideals* and responded on September 15th.

15th
13 Norham Gardens, Oxford

Dear Camac: I have sent on the preface to Mr. Frowde[84] without a word of correction. I have had a remarkable series of letters at intervals from young doctors about the book. The other day I went to Hull and was much interested in the young doctor and his wife. I sent them the book. A letter in reply said it had been their comfort for more than a year.

I am so glad to hear that you have a copy of the Rush book for me—many thanks. I will prize it very highly. Let me know if I can be of any help about your book.[85]

With love to the family. We are just back from Bude.

Sincerely Yours, Wm. Osler

[Camac appended this note: In re C. & I. and to preface to later impression of *Counsels and Ideals*.]

The envelope shows that Osler misaddressed the letter to 108 E. 64th St., New York, instead of 65th St., as he was often to do.

Four months elapsed before Osler next wrote, in January, 1908. This letter was also handwritten.

5th ['o8]
13 Norham Gardens

Dear Camac: Your photo is splendid—a bit stern—but a wonderful picture all the same. Thank you so much. How goes the book? Did you have a chat with Welch? I am sure he could give you many useful points. Let me know if I can be of any service. We have had a very jolly Xmas— Isaac Walton[86] had a couple of boys with him & we got a number of the Rhodes scholars to join us at dinner. The house is most comfortable & it is a delight to have my books at hand. I have been picking up a few treasures here & there. The most interesting bibliographical item is the collection of all Burton's books at Christ Church,[87] about

500, (which were scattered indiscriminately). I have had a copy made of the Burton picture at Brazenose [*sic*][88] and have had it inserted among the books with the 17th cent. editions & the 19th cent. above & below. The Bodleian[89] continues to be a delight. We are hoping for a big grant from the Curzon Fund[90] which will enable us to get a new stack.

Mrs. Osler keeps well & sends love. I hope we may see you next summer. Love to Mrs. Camac & the chicks.

Ever Yours, Wm. Osler

There followed a short time later a typed letter. It contains enigmatic responses to questions which Camac must have asked.

13 Norham Gardens, Oxford.
Jan. 20th, 1908

Dear Camac: I do not believe I ever thanked you for the Rush book which I have been reading with the greatest interest. What a fund of valuable information there is and some of the biographical sketches are remarkable. Did you read about the first Provost Smith?

I am so glad the trypanosomiasis case came to you. I knew you would be interested in it. I should think Manson would be only too glad to allow you to report about it. Do ask Lister. He would be greatly pleased. If you prefer it, I will ask him.

Many thanks for the memorandum. I did thank you for the picture—did I not? It is on my mantelpiece in very good company—next to J. B. S. Jackson.[91]

Love to all at home.

Sincerely yours, Wm. Osler

The following month, on the letterhead of the Regius Professor of Medicine, Oxford, came a brief typewritten note.

From the Regius Professor of Medicine, Oxford.
Feb. 27th, 1908

Dear Camac: I am delighted to hear from Lister that he has accepted your dedication. It is very satisfactory. He seems to be very pleased about it. Have you heard that we are issuing from the Press this year two large volumes of Lister's collected works?[92]

I hope the Lassie is all right.

Sincerely yours, Wm. Osler

Following his return from a continental excursion Osler wrote Camac in response to communications concerning Camac's new book. Some vicissitudes of family and travel are included.

13 Norham Gardens, Oxford.
April 18th, 1908

Dear Camac: Yes! this sort of thing cannot be too simple and I like it very much. What exactly is to be the title of the book.[93] "Epoch Making Contributions to Medicine" sounds very well. Did I understand that you wished me to forward this reply to Lord Lister. I gather that you did, as you have it so carefully addressed. I have done so, in any case.

I have just returned from Vienna,[94] where I went with Pratt to the meeting of the Congress fur Innere Medizin. We had a delightful visit. I enjoyed every minute of it. Mrs. Osler and Revere were to have joined me in Paris, but the young scoundrel took it into his hide to have measles from which he is just convalescent. I hope your little girl is better. Greetings to Mrs. Camac.

Sincerely yours, W. Osler

Camac added a footnote of explanation: "First sentence refers to dedication of Epoch Making Collection to Lord Lister."

In July, 1908 came another typewritten letter from Osler.

> *13 Norham Gardens, Oxford.*
> *July 21st, 1908*

Dear Camac: I shall be glad to see Weir when he turns up. I have the notes of his case when I saw him first in Long Island, just after he was recovering from his angina attack. Considering his very hazardous state, it is remarkable that he has lasted so long. I will let you know what I think of him.

I wish we were at Murray Bay this summer with you. We always look back with great pleasure on the Caribou days. I hope you found your little girl better. I am sending you my Linacre Lecture[95] given at St. John's College, Cambridge, which may interest you. It is high time we had a visit from you. Mrs. Osler and the boy are well.

> *Sincerely yours, Wm. Osler*

In September the next handwritten letter followed. This was filled with news about Osler's upcoming sabbatical year and matters of bookish interest.

> *Sept. 25 ['08]*
> *13 Norham Gardens, Oxford.*

Dear Camac: No I am not in America. I thought I had written about our change of plans. I am taking a sabbatical year & Oct. 1st I am off to Paris where I hope to spend Xmas—then on to Lyons, Montpellier & the North Italian towns—& so south & possibly sail from Naples in May to get over in time for the ass. of am. phys. I am looking forward to the trip with great pleasure. Tommy [Revere] will remain here at school. Mrs. Osler will join me in Paris about the middle of Oct. I am so glad to hear that the Lassie & Mrs. Camac are better. Murray Bay is a great tonic. [undecipherable] book is a great success. I hope by this time you will have had my collected essays, The Alabama Student—the Press issues it in N.Y. Did you get my Linacre?—I am sure you will be interested in it— as you did not mention it there may have been an oversight. Miss Nichols and I got into a mess about the mailing list. I have just finished revising my text book[96]—not a heavy revision & they are not breaking up the plates, still there will be a good deal of new matters. I am glad to see the "Counsels & Sidevils," as I heard it called, has reached a 4th impression & such a success it has had. It is a great disappointment not to be at the Congress[97] but this scheme did not mature until a few weeks ago. Love to the family.

Sincerely yours, Wm. Osler

P.S. I saw Col. Weir in London on his way back from Nauheim[98]—in charge of a Dr. Ward—Pulse regular— heart weak, dyspnea in extreme—but much benefited by the trip.

A postcard from Paris on December 16th, 1908, attested to Osler's enjoyment of his sabbatical.

44 Ave de Jena, 16th
Paris

Dear C, I am sending you a Servetus[99] picture while he was in prison. How is the Epochs getting on? I remain here until Jan 10th. Such a good time—the men have been most kind. I am picking up a good deal in the way of clin. medicine—a few old books but most important of all getting to know the men—Greetings to all at home for the New Year.

Yours ever, W. O.

An undated postcard depicting the Arena at Verona, Italy and misaddressed again to "C.B.N. Camac" on 64th St., rather than 65th St., New York City, was sent in early April 1909. The brief note said simply:

Have turned north—we shall spend Easter in Oxford. I sail about the 18th of April. Will see you soon. Love to the family.

Yours, W. O.

On April 9, 1909, a handwritten letter was dispatched from Oxford. It expressed Osler's excitement at receiving a copy of Camac's new book.[100] It is also filled with news of the visit to Italy.

[April] 9th ['09]
13 Norham Gardens, Oxford

Dear Camac: We got back last eve and prowling among the pile of books on the sofa I came across your fine volume. I had not any idea that it was out—Hearty Congratulations! It is A.1—A for the format & 1 for the matter. It represents a good deal of work, but I think you will be repaid. In the first place you have got together in one volume scattered materials which are very difficult to get at; then you have selected the really great events, and lastly you have let the tale tell itself which is a great matter. I think Lister will be very pleased—His letter is excellent. We have had a splendid winter. Italy was a treat —I saw Rome, but a month is too short a time. Still I have an idea and can go back with intelligence. Florence is most seductive. The Medici Library is the most wonder [?] collection I have ever seen—& in the shelves & desks made by Michael Angelo! Bologne was a great treat. The Univ. Court [?] is unique. I have photos of it for you. Padua was a bit disappointing—Ichabod is written in the portals. I sail next week, so you may have a telephone call any day after the receipt of this. I shall be in N.Y. a few days & then go on to Phila. Boston & Baltimore. We shall have many things to talk about. I hope Mrs. Camac & the lassies are well. Miss McCagg is here with us & sends her greetings.

Mrs. Osler sends love. Tommy is well & fat.

Yours Ever, Wm. Osler

The following day, April 10th, a postal card was written from Oxford. It said:

Your letter arrived this a.m. I posted mine last Eve. This will probably go out on the steamer with me. It will be very nice to have a long chat again. Poor Nicoll![101] I am sorry to hear of his death. You will miss him very much.

You know we are publishing Lister's Opera Omnia.[102] Your book will be a great help. The press is printing in 2 big quarto volumes.

I am glad you liked my letters. I have been so busy that I have not had time to finish the others [?]—hope to do so on the steamer.

Yours, W. O.

Three days later, April 13, 1909, a brief note was written telling of an enforced change of plans.

13th
13 Norham Gardens, Oxford

Dear Camac: I do not sail until the 21st. I was to have left tomorrow but I have a heavy cold and am still in bed. Better today but it would be risky to go off this Eve. to Southampton.

Yours ever, Wm. Osler

On June 17, 1909, Osler wrote from Montreal to ask a favor.

17th [June 1909]
56 Mackay Street, Montreal

Dear Camac: I am off tomorrow by the Empress of B. [Britain]. I have had a bully time here & have seen all my old friends. The new school is splendid. Campbell Howard[103] and Bill[104] are in good form. Marjorie H.[105] and Bill came over with me. I wish we could see you again in Oxford. Perhaps next year. Will you go to Brentano's[106] and ask them to send to Mrs. Robert Brewster[107] S.S. Adriatic White Star on the 23rd.—next Wednesday—Bliss Perry's[108] *Walt Whitman* & Belloc's[109] *Paris* (if B's book is not there any other good description of Paris, as Hare's [?]) & enclose my card. Send me a memo or ask B. to do so.

Yours sincerely, Wm. Osler

The final communication from Osler during 1909, marked in Osler's hand, "from W.O." is a tear sheet from Guy's Hospital Gazette for October 2, 1909. This is page 420 and is "The Student's Guide to Osler." It consists of 14 verses of doggerel, based on Osler's 6th edition of the text-book, and is signed "S.S." The author was H. O. Brockhouse, of Cambridge and Guy's Hospital.

The first and last verses are as follows:

> Some people are keen upon Taylor
>   When studying medicine's wiles,
> While others will steal a few moments with
>   Wheeler
>   — Both excellent books in their styles —
> But give me the text-book of Osler
>   (Or don't, for I've bought it by now!)
> And set *con amore* the laurel of glory
>   On William of Baltimore's brow.

— — — — — — —

And now you are with us at Oxford
    You've plenty of leisure, no doubt, —
So make I petition, another edition,
    And leave the Pathology out;
Cut symptoms and treatment, and give us
    More tales, repartees, epigrams,
It would leave the whole screed more amusing
        to read,
    And quite as much use for exams!

It was not until April 7, 1910, that Osler wrote again. This letter was typed on "Open Arms" stationery.

13 Norham Gardens, Oxford
April 7th, '10

Dear Camac, Perhaps you may have seen Mrs. Osler by this time. She went out to see her brother-in-law, Harry Chapin, who is very ill.

So glad to hear you have got into the University Club,— it must have been over the heads of a good many.

We hope to come out towards the end of July, and shall go to Murray Bay for a few weeks; the boy is anxious to have some fishing and camping. I do not know what arrangements Mrs. Osler is making. We are to go at first to Mrs. McCagg.

I do not know whether I sent you my last papers, my mailing list is in some confusion, if so could you send them on to someone else.

It is nice to see that you have got so much work to do at the Academy, it must be most congenial.

Sincerely yours, Wm. Osler

The next was on the stationery of the Regius Professor of Medicine, Oxford. It was a note of introduction. On it has been written "Foster Kennedy,

128 E. 76," presumably the Irishman being introduced:

> *From the Regius Professor of Medicine, Oxford.*
> *May 5th, '10.*

Dear Camac, Here is a good Irish man, whose forebears
were no doubt chums of yours, (I mean of your ancestors
of course!) He goes out to be with Frantzel and Bailey,
I am sure you will like him.

With kind regards.

> *Sincerely yours, Wm. Osler*

Another hasty typewritten note on the same stationery followed in July:

> *From the Regius Professor of Medicine, Oxford.*
> *July 25th, '10.*

Dear Camac, I hope I may catch you in Murray Bay; we
sail on Friday the 29th, so that we may get there possibly
Saturday afternoon the 6th.

Love to the family.

> *Sincerely yours, Wm. Osler*

Toward the end of the year came another typewritten letter acknowledging Christmas presents
sent and received. The postscript was written by
hand.

> *13 Norham Gardens, Oxford*
> *Dec. 22nd, '10.*

Dear Camac, I am sending you an address which I gave in
Edinburgh on the occasion of the opening of a tuberculosis gathering last year.[110] It will be a bit late for Christmas—but put it down to the binding. You may have
already seen it as Phillips has bothered me for a long time
for something for his magazine, and I thought it might
suit the public.[111]

> *Sincerely yours, Wm. Osler*

[Holograph] Thank the Camac sisters & Co. for their presents—not to be opened till Xmas day.

Interspersed at this point in the correspondence are two handwritten letters from Osler to other physicians. Their provenance is unknown. One is to "Dear Strouse" and is dated December 20, '09. It acknowledges receipt of two papers and congratulates the author on his work. The other, dated 9th, July, 1912 is to "Dear Newmark." It thanks the addressee for his papers on spastic paraplegia and notes that, "Dear old J. B. S. Jackson of Boston used to say that one of the most important things for a clinician is to keep the 'run' of his cases."

In January, 1911, Osler sent the daughter of an old fellow-student to see Camac with the following note of introduction:

> *From the Regius Professor of Medicine, Oxford.*
> *Jan. 14th, '11.*

Dear Camac, This letter will be sent to you by Miss Helen Locke (the daughter of a very old and dear fellow student of mine, the late Dr. Locke),[112] a graduate of the Presbyterian Training School, who is beginning private nursing in New York. Please put her on your list; she is very capable and well trained. I know you would find her satisfactory in every way.

> *Sincerely yours, Wm. Osler*

A few days later he sent an annotated, typewritten note from Oxford.

> *13 Norham Gardens, Oxford*
> *Jan. 23rd, [1911]*

Dear Camac, Dr. Thursfield one of the juniors at St. Bartholomew's Hospital sails on the *Lusitania* Baltic on the 29th on a tour of inspection of the U.S. Clinics. Their address in New York will be the *American Express Company,* N. Y. If you get this in time you might send him a line to the steamer & help arrange their program.

Sincerely yours, Wm. Osler

Get them put up at U.C. [University Club].
Love to the business girls & Mrs. C.

["Lusitania" was crossed out and "Baltic" inserted in pencil. The last half of the final sentence was also pencilled in, as was the postscript.]

Another note at the top, written in by hand says: "I am off to Egypt for 2 months with my brother — E.B."[113]

A postcard dated 28th (Jan., 1911) corrects misinformation contained in a previous letter.

Dr. Thursfield & his friends sail on the Baltic tomorrow not the Lusitania as I wrote. Love to the Camac sisters & Co.

Yours, Wm. Osler

Next came a picture postcard depicting the Karnak Obelisk.[114] This, Camac notes, was received in February, 1911. The message states:

Wish you were here. Such a wonderful place—even in its ruins. We are having a delightful trip—such sunshine. Love to the family. Greetings to Camac sisters & Co.

W. O.

Shortly afterward another postcard, this one a color photograph of the Mosque of Mohammed Ali, Cairo, bore the message:

On way up the Nile with E.B.O. & party—delighted. I hope all goes well with you and yours. Love to the firm. I hope they are making money in these good times.

W. O.

Oxford Days Following Baronetcy

1911-1919

IN SEPTEMBER he wrote by hand a newsy letter about families and the new edition of his textbook (Fig. 14).

> Sept. 12th, 1912
> 13 Norham Gardens, Oxford
> [Embossed letterhead]

Dear Camac: I hope Mrs. Camac is better [she suffered from severe, lifelong arthritis.] I was so sorry to hear that she continued to be so wretched. How are the lassies? Is the business increasing? I must send them a large order soon. You will have shortly—Ed. 8th of my text book— much changed, I hope for the better! I am not coming out this fall—my Yale lectures[115] have been postponed until the Spring. I am glad as it will enable me to be present at the opening of the new psychopathic Institute at the JHH.[116] We have had a good holiday in Scotland. Revere has grown so much 2 inches taller than I am, a dear, good, fellow but no student.

Give my love to your wife & the girls.

Ever yours, W. O.

This letter, once more, had been addressed to 64th St. instead of 65th St.

Intervals between letters were getting longer but he still managed to keep them personal. Osler seemed never to forget the children. The game that he kept playing with them through his letters to Dr. Camac was characteristic of the way he related

to children. He played their games with the same
devotion and apparent sincerity which the children
gave them. The next letter attests to this (Fig. 15).

> *From the Regius Professor of Medicine, Oxford.*
> *29th Jan. 1913*

Dear Camac, It was very nice to get your letter this morning, and last evening the report on the Ottawa typhoid,
which is most interesting.

I am so glad to hear that Mrs. Camac is better. What a
sad time she has had! I shall get out in time for the
meeting on the 16th of April,[117] and a day or two before
that you may expect a telephone call, and I shall of course
run around and see you at once. Give my love to the girls
and say that I am sorry I have had to stop all business
relations with their firm, because of the sand in the sugar.
I hope the opening of the new milinery department will
be ready by the time I get out. Revere is very well. He has
left Winchester this term to have a year's tutoring in
Latin and Greek, in which he is weak, for his entrance
examination.

With love to you all.

> *Sincerely yours, W. O.*

A letter from Camac to Lady Osler, dated May 9,
1913, helps fill in the story of the relationship between mentor and student, as well as that of *Counsels and Ideals.* The fact that Camac sent it with a
covering letter to Osler for delivery to Mrs. Osler
also tells something of the timorous nature of Dr.
Camac. The two letters follow, first that to Dr. Osler
from Camac (Fig. 16).

> *May 9th, 1913*

My dear Dr. Osler, Would you hand the enclosed note to
Mrs. Chief?

You know I have always been an awkward citizen at

arrived. Fortunately Revere
was at home & we got
out the Macmalodon & had
up stairs but the common
bill of smoke & very hot. No
damage to the books
R. very well, writing
orders, at Canniers the No 3 field
ambulance, near Poperings.
Much interest from the Cost.
particularly the Paris-T's
Love to us all

Ever yours

Wm Osler

$$ 2 \, \smile $$

13, NORHAM GARDENS,
OXFORD.

Dear Camac

Greeting,
& love to Jim & Gwen
for 1916. Thanks for
the Galtherie charming
letter. Twill help the
little book shop. We had
a deuce of a scare the
other night – dining room
ablaze. & practically burnt
out before the firemen

3014   1915 - 16
22DEC15

Dr Camac
128 E 60 St
New York
U.S.c.

OPENED BY
CENSOR.

Figure 18. Letter from Osler to
Camac telling him of a fire in his
home. Camac states that he did
not send this letter to Cushing
with the others. The envelope is
stamped, "Opened by the Censor."

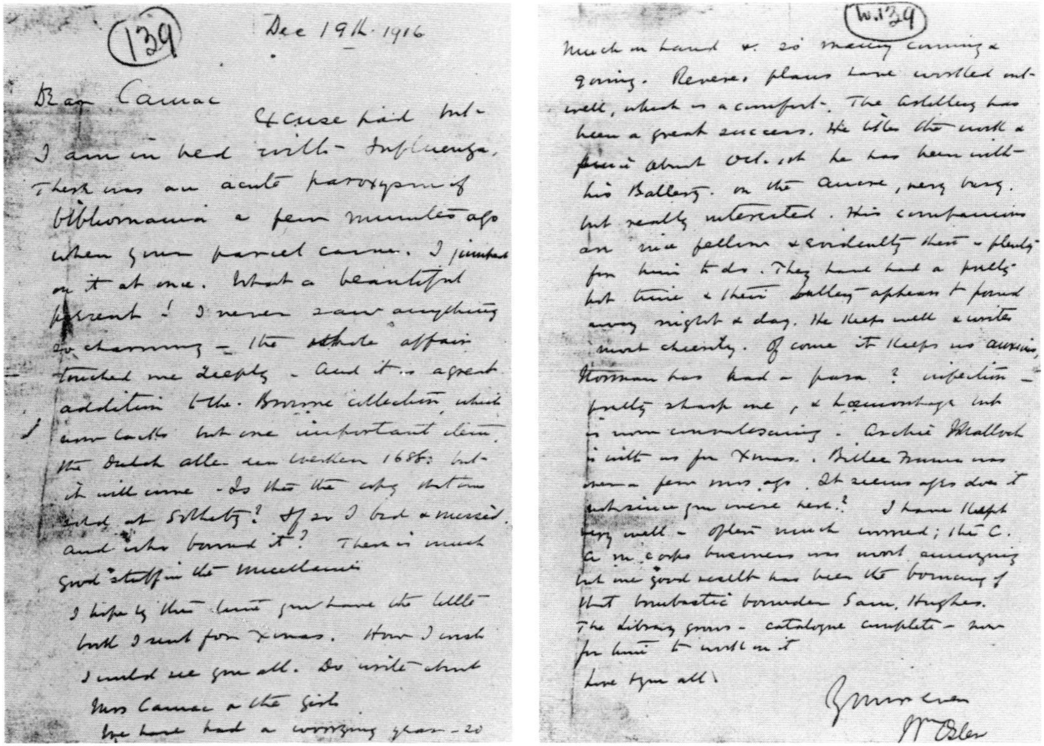

Figure 19. Jubilant letter from Osler on receipt of the gift of the 1683 edition of Browne's, *Certain Miscellany Tracts* from a group of American friends.

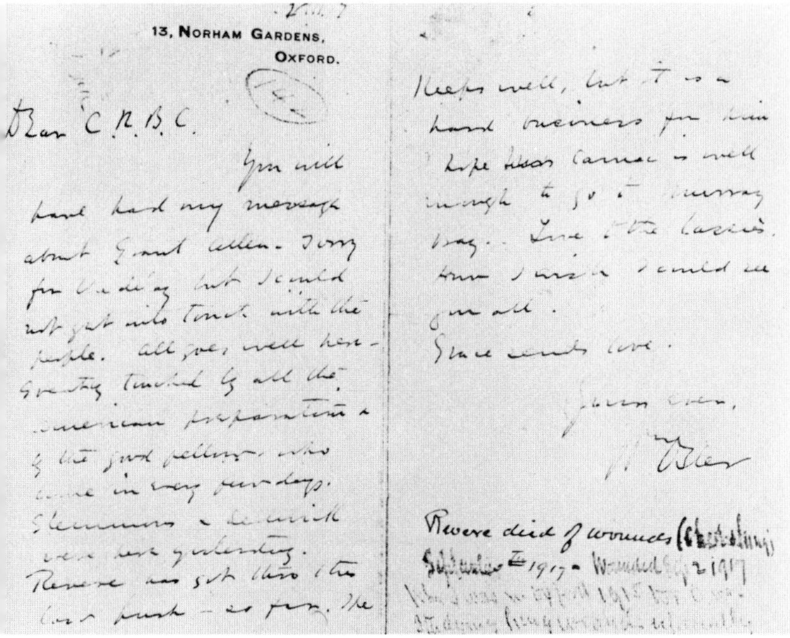

Figure 20A. Last hand-written letter in the collection from Osler to Camac, with Camac's footnote about Revere's death. See page 105.

Figure 20B. Last photograph of Edward Revere Osler, in military
uniform, shortly before his death from war injuries.

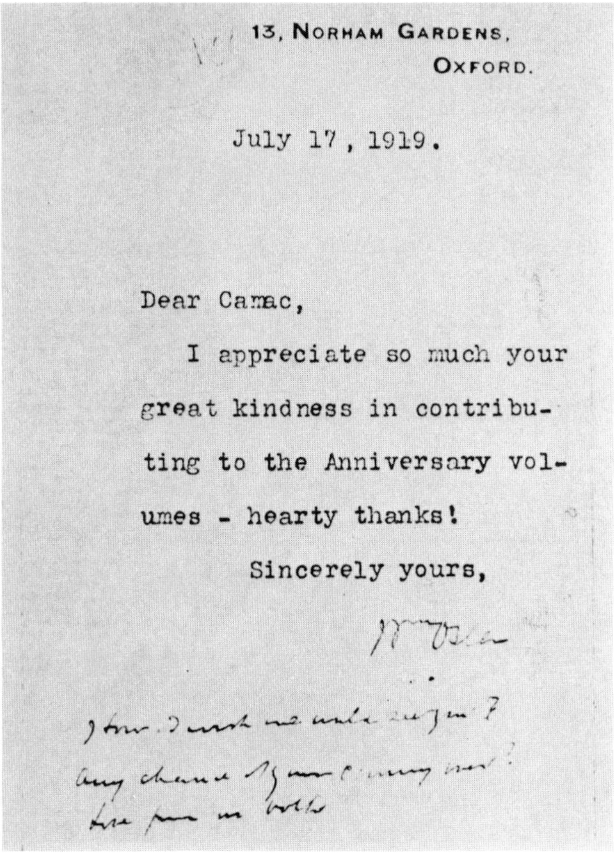

13, NORHAM GARDENS,
OXFORD.

July 17, 1919.

Dear Camac,

I appreciate so much your
great kindness in contributing to the Anniversary volumes - hearty thanks!

Sincerely yours,

Figure 21. Last note from Osler to Camac.

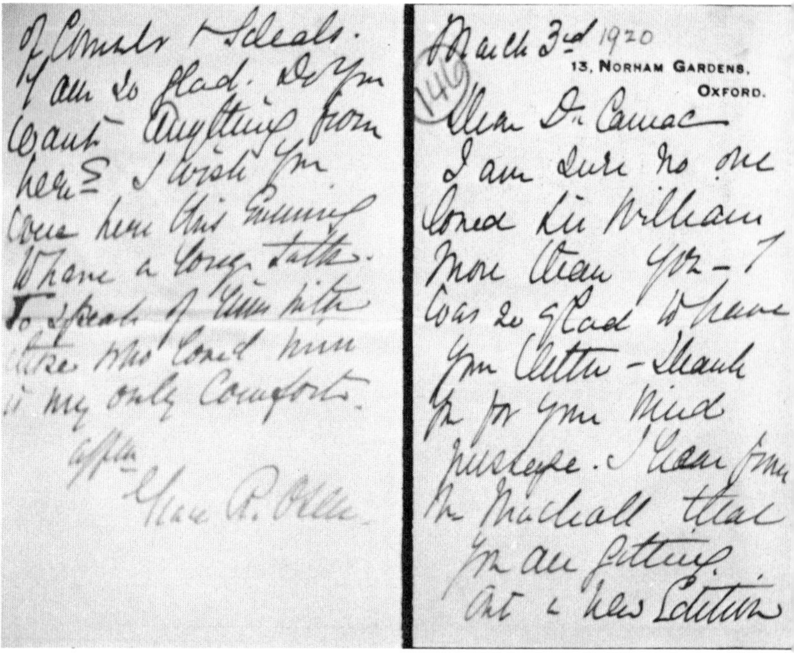

March 3rd 1920

13, Norham Gardens,
Oxford.

Dear Dr Camac

I am sure no one loved Sir William more than you — I was so glad to have your letter — thank you for your kind message. I hear from Mr Malloch that you are getting out a new Edition of Counsels & Ideals. I am so glad. Do you want anything from here? I wish you could come here this evening & have a long talk. To speak of him with those who loved him is my only comfort.

Affly
Grace R. Osler

Figure 22. First letter from Lady Osler to Camac following the death of her husband.

COUNSELS
AND IDEALS

FROM THE WRITINGS OF
WILLIAM OSLER

SECOND EDITION

HUMPHREY MILFORD
OXFORD UNIVERSITY PRESS
LONDON   NEW YORK   TORONTO   MELBOURNE
CAPE TOWN   BOMBAY   CALCUTTA   MADRAS
SHANGHAI   PEKING   COPENHAGEN
1921

Figure 23. Title page and frontispiece of second edition of
Counsels and Ideals.

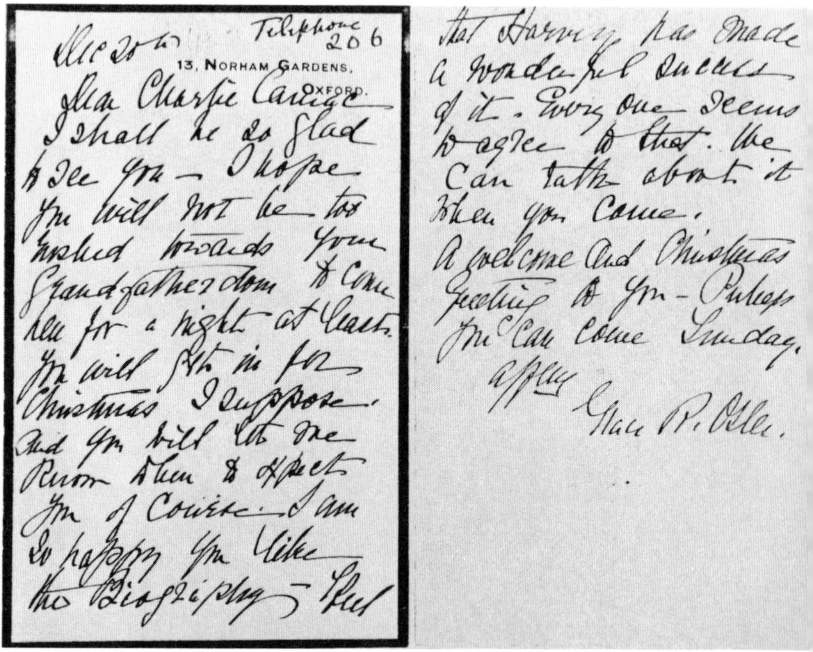

Figure 24. Penultimate letter from Lady Osler to Camac.

Figure 25. Lady Osler and her sister, Mrs. Chapin, shortly before
Lady Osler's death.

Figure 26. A photograph of Dr. C. N. B. Camac in his yard in
Altadena, California, in his later years.

expressing appreciation. Well I have not improved—So I can only say "Thank You" for cheer & encouragement to my wife.

Affectionately, C. N. B. Camac

May 9, 1913

My dear Mrs. Chief: In 1905 when I was in Oxford The Chief and I planted some seeds[118] which have yielded fruit; just how much this has been is hard to estimate— That many hungry souls have been fed by this fruit is attested to by the letters & expressions I get every year— Besides this soul feeding success the planting has yielded practical returns. I have waited till these took on some proportions & while these are yet modest I want you & The Chief to have them. If you know of some book he wants and something you would like to get for yourself with this little figure will you please be the middleman and turn the trick.

As usual The Chief managed to attend to everything & see everybody during his short stay—My wife was greatly cheered by his visits to her. She is now among the "shut-ins" but like so many of them she has a place & thought for others which makes an atmosphere peculiar in its influence upon the busy out worker.

I hear good reports of Revere—If you bring him to Murray Bay we will show him some Wood Life—I hope the Murray Bay plan will work out & that we will have you all for a stay here—

Sincerely, C. N. B. Camac

Accompanying Camac's letter to Lady Osler was a memorandum of Exchange from Brown Brothers & Co. of New York for $100.00, the dividend from *Counsels and Ideals* referred to in the letter.

Lady Osler's response came a month later, from a spa, evidently delayed by her husband's tardiness in delivering Camac's letter to her.

Granby Hotel, Harrogate
June 10th [1913]

Dear Dr. Camac: Our Chief did not give me your letter very promptly—hence the delay in your hearing from me. I hardly know what to say—how to thank you for what you have done and for the tender thought & feeling that made you do it. It touches me deeply. The book [see note 118] has always seemed a welding link in our friendship and the work was associated with that first summer when we were finding ourselves in our new life. There is a book Sir William is looking at just now and I think he must have it and the value will be doubled—I really do appreciate this so much. I am so glad to hear Mrs. Camac is happy— I think of you both so often in this trial. I may have to come to her for a lesson. I am here for a cure—something wrong with both wrists. Mrs. McCagg will tell you. With wishes for a happy summer I am affectionately

Grace R. Osler

Osler next dictated a letter in July after Lady Osler returned from the spa. He "thinks" she has the gout.

From the Regius Professor of Medicine, Oxford.
25th July, 1913

Dear Camac, Thanks so much for your sketch of McClellan. It is sad that he should have been cut off so comparatively early. I remember him with great pleasure: he was always so kind to me.

I do hope Mrs. Camac is better. Grace has returned from Harrogate, and her wrists are much more supple. I think it is the gout, as she has had attacks of swelling in her big toe.

We are busy getting ready for the congress.[119] I have a very heavy job as President of the Medical Section. There will be a number of nice men here: I wish you could have come. T. McCrae and his wife have just left us after a short visit. Willie McCallum has been here, and I expect young Shattuck[120] for Sunday. Do give my love to Mrs. Camac and the girls.

Sincerely yours, Wm. O.

The next letter must have been typed by a new secretary (identifying initials never were used); Camac's name was misspelled in two instances and corrected by Osler.

> *From the Regius Professor of Medicine, Oxford.*
> *17, Sept. 1913*

Dear Camac, So nice to hear from you. We have had news at intervals from Mrs. McCagg. I am sorry to hear that Mrs. Camac has not been benefited by the summer. It is too bad. Give my love to her and to the girls.

The Congress was a great success. Cushing's address[121] was splendid. We have just returned from Scotland, where Revere had fairly good fishing. I suppose by this time you are back in New York, settled for the winter.

Love to you all.

Sincerely yours, Wm. O.

Billy Francis is here for a short trip—looking very well.

A typed letter on the crested letterhead of the Regius Professor, dated 24 Jan. 1914 began with the salutation "Dear Doctor." Over this Osler wrote "Camac." The letter introduced a friend from Paris.

> *From the Regius Professor of Medicine, Oxford.*
> *24, Jan. 1914*

Dear Doctor [Camac], My friend Dr. Monod of Paris has been appointed by the French Government to report on the methods of postgraduate teaching in the United States. Will you please give him every possible help! He will be in New York from Feb. 15 to Feb. 22nd, c/o American Express Company.

Sincerely yours, Wm. Osler

[Note by hand:] Love to Mrs. Camac and the girls.

Monod is an A.1. man—member of the old Hugenot [sic] family; & talks English like a native. I have written to the President of the Academy as M. is prepared to lecture on P.G. Education in Paris.

Camac's response is of interest with respect to the state of postgraduate education in New York at that time.

128 East 60th Street,
New York, Feb. 11th, 1914

Sir William Osler,
Oxford, England.

My dear Dr. Osler, I will be on the look out for Dr. Monod of Paris.

I wish New York had something to offer in Post Graduate teaching. I fear at present it is a case of studying "snakes in Ireland."

In the belated Christmas mails there came your remembrance. With all those that you have to remember, it is good not to be forgotten. Thank you.

I hope nothing has changed your plans regarding Murray Bay for next Summer. We are looking forward to seeing you.

My wife's general condition has improved somewhat. She sends a great deal of love.

Sincerely yours, C. N. B. Camac

P.S. Would it be possible to have your Secretary send me the reprints of your articles of recent years.

Another letter from Camac ten days later expressed his pleasure in meeting Monod and having him in New York, as well as learning about what Osler had done for Monod.

128 E. 60th Street
New York, Feb. 21st, 1914

My dear Dr. Osler, Monod arrived last week, and we are all delighted with him. I hope he got hold of some material in New York for his good work.

He told me about his M.R.C.P. and his being the first Frenchman to receive this degree,—all very modestly.

I should conclude that you had outdone Napoleon in this invasion of England by the French. It will be a great thing if you have taken down the first bar of the inter-national fence in Science.

Thank you for the opportunity of meeting Monod.

Sincerely yours, C. N. B. Camac

Osler's next letter, written, no doubt, before re-ceiving these two letters from Camac, addresses him for the first time more familiarly than the usual, "Dear Camac."

From the Regius Professor of Medicine, Oxford.
25, Feb. 1914

Dear C.N.B., So nice to hear that Mrs. Camac is more comfortable. I wish she could get a set of new hinges. Give my love to the members of the firm. I suppose they are growing rapidly.

We have had a very busy winter—so many visitors—and I have been occupied with a number of things. We are getting the Historical Section of the Royal Society of Medicine into very good shape. Our plans for the summer are uncertain. I had hoped to be able to get out early, but the National Library Association meets here at the invita-tion of the Curators of the Bodleian, so that I do not think I can possibly leave until after the meeting, which is at the end of August. I do not know what Grace and Revere will do.

Sincerely yours, Wm. Osler

Camac included two more of his letters to Osler written in March, 1914, in the collection. In the first Camac discussed an interesting case of paralysis with recovery in a child which each had seen. In the second, dated March 24, 1914, Camac described the child in more detail after examining her again. The first letter follows:

128 East 60th St., New York,
March 18, 1914

My dear Dr. Osler, Thank you for your letter and the reprints, which I am glad to get.

"The Medical Clinic" arouses many happy memories.

Every lover of libraries and books will be delighted to hear that you are in the work of the Bodleian organization. I recall so well the librarian's (was his name Nicolls?) remark that the library would not be adequate to the needs of modern students till the shackles of old time cumbersome systems were thrown off. He seemed to despair of the Possibility of ridding the Library of these trammels and hinted that some of the obstacles were in the flesh.

I hope the great Hopkins celebration will draw you to this country.

Mr. Fielder, whose little daughter you saw in my office, telephoned me that the child had suddenly felt a little pain in the left hip and, a few hours later, walked without assistance. He has suggested bringing her for me to see, in order that I may write you more fully. The joy in the man's voice was a bit of music which I have carried in mind for many days.

Please give my love to Mrs. Chief.

Sincerely yours, C.N.B. Camac

Osler responded on 3, April, 1914, expressing his amazement at the child's improvement.

> *From the Regius Professor of Medicine, Oxford*
> *3 April, 1914*

Dear Camac, I do not see what in Heaven's name could have been the condition there. It looked like one of those hopelessly incurable cases. It certainly should be worked up carefully and reported. I think we have to revise our prognosis in these cases of widespread poliomyelitis. The recovery which some of them make is remarkable.

I hope Mrs. Camac is keeping pretty well.

Love to the girls.

> *Sincerely yours, Wm. Osler*

Still thinking of the case, Osler wrote again two weeks later.

> *From the Regius Professor of Medicine, Oxford.*
> *16, April, 1914.*

Dear Camac, Do find out from Mr. Fiedler [*sic*] the names of the doctors who saw his daughter—I think he said Sachs[122] had—as it would be very important to get the full notes of the case and to have it published. As you say, if it had happened in Christian Science hands, it would have been a boom.

Have you got Friend's [*sic*] "History of Physic"? If not, I should like to send you it.

> *Sincerely yours, Wm. Osler*

Love to the family. I hope Mrs. Camac keeps fully comfortable.

Camac responded on April 24, 1914, naming Dr. Henry S. Stearns[123] as a physician who had seen the child with paralysis and detailing other news.

128 E. 60th Street, New York,
April 24, 1914

My dear Dr. Osler, I have not Mr. Fielder's address, but one physician whom I know he had his daughter see was Henry S. Stearns, 45 W. 58th St., New York.

Thank you for enquiring about Julia. She has been away to the seashore for a month in preparation for enormous doses of vaccine which it is proposed to give her on her return. Her general condition seems to have improved considerably.

I am sailing for Europe with my brother on May 16th, to be gone a few weeks. My brother and his wife go direct to Paris and will remain on the Continent, but I am hoping to run over to England, as the Dean of the Columbia Medical School has commissioned me to look up the graduate teaching both in France and England.

I expect to see Monod, who has given me a letter to Rist.

No, I have not a copy of Friend's [sic] "History of Physic," and I should indeed like to have one.

Sincerely yours, C.N.B. Camac

On May 4, 1914, Osler responded with a brief typewritten note, again using the more familiar salutation but reversing the initials as he so often did:

From the Regius Professor of Medicine, Oxford
4, May, 1914

Dear C. B. N., Glad to hear that we shall see you soon. Come directly to us either from Plymouth or Southampton. It will be a great treat to see you again. So glad to hear that Mrs. Camac is better.

I am sending you the copy of Friend's Physic.

Sincerely yours, Wm. Osler

Another similar note followed on May 25. This one was addressed to Hotel Chatham, Rue Daunon, Paris.

From the Regius Professor of Medicine, Oxford
25 May, 1914

Dear Camac, Delighted to hear from you. We shall expect
you whenever you care to come. I shall be at home all the
summer—I do not sail until the 7th of September. I am
sure you will have a delightful trip.

Ever Yours, Wm. Osler
(W.H.E.)
[signed and initialed by secretary]

A newspaper clipping from an unknown source
is inserted here:

French Honor Sir William Osler

Paris, June 2 [1914] — Sir William Osler, Regius Professor
of Medicine at Oxford University, has been elected a
Foreign Associate of the Academy of Medicine.

On July 19, 1914, Osler telegraphed Camac at 53
Victoria Rd., Kensington: "Do come tomorrow or
Sunday. Join Sister here Monday for luncheon.[124]
Must see more of you." Lady Osler added her invi-
tation to that of Sir William:

13, Norham Gardens, Oxford
June 12th [1914]

Dear Dr. Camac, I have a horrible feeling that Sir William
hasn't answered your letter. He has been rushed to death
and muddled with things & people. Of course you must
come to us the minute you can—and stay as long as you
can. Do let *me* know your plans—I do not always know
from the consulting room table the comings or goings
of people.

Affect., Grace R. Osler

Osler's next long typewritten letter, dated 16 October 1914, reflects the ominous events that were

taking place. Camac evidently had appealed to Osler for help in volunteering his services.

From the Regius Professor of Medicine, Oxford
16, October, 1914

Dear Camac, It is awfully good of you to offer your services. I wish there were some good billet, but the places I know are all full. There is, as yet, no scarcity on the medical side, but later, when these 600,000 men are settled as regiments, there will be a demand. Of course, one difficulty in official positions, is that a man must be a British subject. If anything really good should turn up, I will let you know at once.

I hope Mrs. Camac is better. My love to her and to the girls.

We are very busy, as you may suppose. Grace has been helping to settle some twelve Louvain professors and their families. We have had a splendid response from America to our appeal.[125] It has been an awful tragedy for these poor souls, many of whom are absolutely destitute. I have just got back from Folkestone, near which we have opened our Canadian Hospital. It has just been filled with Belgian wounded.

Revere has come up to Christ Church and is in the training camp.

Yours, W. O.

Another letter, three weeks later, relates to activities connected with the war.

From the Regius Professor of Medicine, Oxford.
6, November, 1914.

Dear Camac, Of course, the difficulty is to get a berth that would be at all suitable. I will, of course, bear it in mind.

I have been trying to get the Government to undertake a systematic study and collection of experiences of the war, but the officials of the Army Medical Department are terribly overworked.

Things are gradually getting into good shape, and the ambulance work at the front has improved enormously. The outlook, too, is much more hopeful.

Love to Mrs. Camac and the girls from us both.

Sincerely yours, Wm. Osler

The next communication finds Camac in England. It is a telegram addressed to Sir William Osler, 53 Victoria Rd., Kensington from Paignton and signed "Beal."[126] It says, "Expect Dr. Carmac [*sic*] tomorrow." Beneath, Camac has written: "1915 — World War. This telegram sent to my sister's house in London notified me to report for duty at the Paignton War Hospital where I served on the Medical Staff (Fig. 17). Beal was the Director of the Hospital."

Lady Osler wrote Camac at The American Woman's War Hospital,[127] Paignton, S. Devon, on July 29, 1915.

> *13 Norham Gardens, Oxford*
> *Thursday*

Dear Dr. Camac, Sir William asks me to send this on to you as he is just leaving for town & thinks you will be interested to go. I hope you have found something profitable at Paignton. Do go abroad—You will have such a good glimpse—if you are near Boulogne be sure to see our boys at the McGill Hospital near Staples. Norman Gwyn is ill with an infected arm at No. 7 General (British) at Boulogne.

We hope to see you here again.

Affectionately, Grace R. Osler

Phoebe sends her love.

On August 9, 1915, a telegram from Osler to Camac at Paignton said: "Leaving for Cardiff Wednesday. Glad you heard from Dr. Page.[128] Come here Tuesday."

Another telegram from Osler in Oxford was addressed to Camac, Steamer, Liverpool-New York, on 1 September, 1915. It stated:

Sorry not to have seen you again. Bon Voyage.

Camac notes at the bottom of the telegram: "As I was leaving to N.Y. after volunteer military service in England and Belgium, 1915."

On December 22, 1915, Osler wrote Camac by hand on "Open Arms" stationery, recounting a near disaster. Camac notes that he did not send this letter to Cushing with the others, when he was writing *The Life*. He does not say why. On the back of the envelope there is a stamped notation: "Opened by the censor" (Fig. 18).

> 22nd *[Dec., 1915]*
> *13, Norham Gardens, Oxford*
>
> *Dear Camac:* Greetings & love to you & yours for 1916. Thanks for Le Galliene's charming letter.[129] 'Twill help the little book shelf. I've had a deuce of a scare the other night—dining room ablaze & practically burnt out before the firemen arrived. Fortunately Revere was at home & we got out the Incanabula & Mss. up stairs but the room was full of smoke & very hot. No damage to the books. R. very well, waiting orders at Camien for the No. 3 Field Ambulance, near Poperinge. Much of interest from the East—particularly the Para-T.'s.[130] Love to you all.
>
> *Ever yours, Wm. Osler*

Inserted here in the correspondence are six letters from Dr. Thomas R. Boggs,[131] of Baltimore. The first letter of November 9, 1916, explains the correspondence, which concerns a proposed gift for Osler.

> *Dr. Thos. R. Boggs,*
> *21 West Chase Street, Baltimore. Nov 9 - '16*

Dear Camac, A small group of Dr. Osler's friends (15) are joining in sending him for Xmas an almost unique copy (only 3 known including this) of the 1683 Browne's "Miscellany Tracts." This perfect copy has been bought at auction after approval of *Cushing* & Mr. Putnam[132] (Librarian of Congress), who says he will take if we don't want it, by my cousin L. L. Mackall an accomplished bibliophile & friend of the Chief's. The cost with transportation will be approx. $150.00. Welch, Thayer, Barker, Hurd, Thomas, Futcher & I are in it here.[133] If you would like to join us send me $10.00 at your early convenience as we want to get it over in time for Xmas as a surprise. Mackall, Cushing, Worthington, Ford & McCrae[134] will also contribute.

> *Sincerely yours, Thos. R. Boggs*

The remainder of the correspondence relates to details of getting signatures, insurance, and shipping arrangements. Camac arranged to have the book shipped in the diplomatic pouch "to escape the chance of being roughly handled by the censors in the examination of packages and the danger of submarines."

The auction catalogue noted the following concerning the 1683 edition of *Certain Miscellany Tracts*. "The genuine first edition, of which only two copies have come up for sale, one of which lacked the portrait. This edition was unquestionably intended for presentation purposes only—."

Osler's joy was expressed in a long, handwritten letter dated Dec. 19th, [1916] (Fig. 19).

Dec. 19th, 1916

Dear Camac, Excuse hand but I am in bed with influenza. There was an acute paroxysm of bibliomania a few minutes ago when your parcel came. I jumped on it at once. What a beautiful present! I never saw anything so charming—the whole affair touched me deeply—And it is a great addition to the Browne collection which now lacks but one important item, the Dutch Alle den Werken 1688, but it will come—Is this the copy that was sold at Sotheby's?[135] If so I bid & missed and who found it? There is much good stuff in the miscelanni.

I hope by this time you have the little book I sent for Xmas. How I wish I could see you all. Do write about Mrs. Camac & the girls.

We have had a worrying year—so much on hand & so many coming & going. Revere's plans have worked out well, which is a comfort. The artillery has been a great success. He likes the work & since about Oct. 1st he has been with his Battery on the Ancre, very busy but really interested. His companions are nice fellows & evidently there is plenty for him to do. They have had a pretty hot time & their battery appears to pound away night & day. He keeps well & writes most cheerily. Of course it keeps us anxious. Norman[136] has had a para ? infection—pretty sharp one, & haemorrhage but is now convalescing. Archie Malloch[137] is with us for Xmas. Billie Francis[138] was over a few mos. ago. It seems a yr does it not since you were here? I have kept very well—often much worried; the C. A. M. Corps[139] business was most annoying but one good result has been the bouncing of that bombastic bounder Sam Hughes. The Library grows—catalogue complete—now for time to work on it.

Love to you all.

Yours Ever, Wm. Osler

At this point in the collection of letters is inserted a series of letters exchanged between Camac and the librarians of the New York Academy of Medicine and the Surgeon General's Library. Camac wished to secure a copy of the 1683 *Certain Miscellany Tracts* for an exhibit for the Charaka Club. They could find no record of such an edition and supplied instead a copy of the 1684 edition from the Surgeon General's Library.

The next letter from Osler, written by hand, was dated August 8, 1917. Camac wrote on it that it was received at Fort Sill, Oklahoma.

8 VIII 17
13 Norham Gardens, Oxford

Dear C. N. B. C., You will have had my message about Grant Allen—Sorry for the delay but I could not get into touch with the people. All goes well here. Greatly touched by all the American preparation & by the good fellows who come in every few days. Slemmons & Sedwich[140] were here yesterday. Revere has got thro this last push— so far. He keeps well, but it is a hard business for him. I hope Mrs. Camac is well enough to go to Murray Bay. Love to the Lassies. How I wish I could see you all.

Grace sends love.

Yours Ever, W. Osler

Camac added a grim footnote to the letter:

"Revere died of wounds September 10, 1917. Wounded Sept. 2, 1917. When I was in Oxford 1915 Dr. O. was studying lung wounds especially" (Fig. 20, A & B).

There was only one other brief typewritten note from Osler after this. It was written two years later (Fig. 21).

13 Norham Gardens, Oxford
July 17, 1919.

Dear Camac, I appreciate so much your great kindness in contributing to the Anniversary volumes—hearty thanks!

Sincerely yours, Wm. Osler

By hand: How I wish we could see you. Any chance of your coming over? Love from us both.

Camac noted that this refers to the two-volume collection of *Contributions to Medical and Biological Research* published in 1919 by Paul B. Hoeber in honor of Osler's 70th birthday.

Correspondence with Lady Osler

1920-1928

MOST OF THE remaining entries in the collection are bordered with black and are from Lady Osler. It was as though Sir William died with Revere, as far as Camac was concerned, for the final personal letter from him was that one written barely two weeks before Revere's wounding. It is unlikely that Camac would have destroyed any letters written between that time and Osler's own death two years and three months later. None survive, in any case, except for the 1919 letter of thanks.

The next letter, numbered by Camac in chronological sequence, is number 144 and was written by an old friend of Camac, C. G. S. Wolf, Professor of Chemistry at Cambridge, England. It is dated January 3, 1920, two days after the memorial services for Sir William Osler.

1 Selwyn Gardens, Cambridge.

Dear Charles, I thought you would like to know that I saw the last of all that was mortal of dear W. O.

I wanted to write you night before last when I came home but I arrived too late to do so, and yesterday came an urgent call to London and again I arrived home very late.

It was a short but very auspicious service. Everyone was there from all over the Country. During his all too short life in England he made a place for himself such as no man of my knowledge has ever made. His loss is a very deep one and to those of us who had the advantage of his personal friendship it is irreparable. It seems impossible to realize that he has gone for he had the wonderful gift of eternal youth. One could never look upon him as an old man.

Jo' and I are off for ten days to the Continent tomorrow. Poor girl, the war has hit her as it has most of us. She has worked unceasingly and is paying the penalty. I am in hope the trip will do her good.

Everything goes well here. I have been appointed Assistant Director of the Institute for the study of animal nutrition in the University and have plenty of interesting work on hand.

My love to you and all in your house.

3.1.20   *Ever, Charles*

Camac waited until February 3, 1920, before expressing his condolence.

Dear Lady Osler, Flooded as you certainly are with messages from all over the world it has seemed the part of those who feel deeply with you to be silent—yet I know you will forgive the sending of this word, for to be silent altogether hurts too much not to seek relief in thus speaking out a few words.

Affectionately, C. N. B. Camac

76 East 56th St.
Feb. 3, 1920.

To which Lady Osler responded on March 3rd, 1920 (Fig. 22):

13 Norham Gardens, Oxford
March 3rd [1920]

Dear Dr. Camac, I am sure no one loved Sir William more than you—I was so glad to have your letter—Thank you for your kind message. I hear from Mr. Mackall that you are getting out a new Edition of Counsels & Ideals. I am so glad. Do you want anything from here? I wish you were here this evening to have a long talk. To speak of him with those who loved him is my only comfort.

Affectionately, Grace R. Osler

By June she was becoming involved with thoughts of "the memoir" which she had been considering. She had gotten Cushing to consent to do it and wrote Camac about the project.

13 Norham Gardens, Oxford
June 12th [1920]

Dear Charlie Camac, Thank you so much for sending me your tender words about our Beloved. How are you getting on with Counsels & Ideals? I am expecting Harvey Cushing in July and I fancy we shall be very busy reading & writing up all details for the Biography—I hope you will come sometime—although you will find it very sad here —What a changed world!

Affecly, Grace R. Osler

She wrote again on October 22, 1920, concerning the dedication for the second edition of *Counsels and Ideals.* She spoke of her sadness and the hope that an epidemic might shorten her suffering. She also spoke of the work she and Harvey Cushing were doing on *The Life* and the effect on her of thus "exposing" her beloved.

13 Norham Gardens, Oxford.
Oct. 22nd [1920]

Dear Charlie Camac, I heard from Mr. Milford yesterday and was shocked when you had not heard from me— I wrote from Southbourne[?] on Sea when I was staying with the Campbell Howards—Letters have sometimes gone astray but my feeble and exhausted brain went nearly permanently astray after 6 weeks work with the beloved exposed [undeciphered] Harvey Cushing & so you will forgive me if I am mistaken. I wrote Mr. Milford at once that I was pleased with the dedication but asked him to add the Edward to the Revere Osler. It was most dear of you—and I know how sincere your feeling is about it all. I shall await the new edition impatiently.

I wish I could see you—I am well but desperately lonely. *Nothing* can help—but the time isn't long fortunately & perhaps an epidemic will shorten it for me. At the moment we are enveloped in darkness in England and no one knows what may happen.

I hope all is well with you and that Mrs. Camac is free from pain these days—keep a knowledge of me before your girls *please.*

Always affecly, Grace R. Osler

Mr. Humphrey Milford, manager of the Oxford University Press, had written Camac in March that Lady Osler was anxious that a new edition of *Counsels and Ideals* be produced.[141] He also told him "privately" that Osler had left a note on a blotting pad on his deathbed stating that a new edition "might be useful" (Fig. 23).

On May 18th, 1921, Lady Osler again wrote, still using her black-bordered letterhead and envelope. She expressed her pleasure and satisfaction with the new edition. There was considerable family news also. She nostalgically noted that her letter was being written on the sixteenth anniversary of their departure from America for Oxford.

May 18th [1921]

Dear Charlie Camac, My copies of "Counsels & Ideals" have arrived at last. They have been wandering some where. I am very, very pleased with the new edition & send you my most affectionate thanks. I hear that every one likes the book.

Sixteen years today since we sailed forth to make our new home. How little I thought it would end like this! You came so soon after. Every day seems to have some association.

I had a delightful letter from Harriet not long ago and am answering it very soon. I was much touched at her writing & at her remembering me. I am glad that you are keeping all of the memories green. When are you coming over?

My sister Mrs. Chapin is with me now & I have had a wonderful visit from my brother who had never been in England before. Mrs. McCagg speaks of coming over but I cannot encourage anyone to come under present conditions—everything is too unsettled.

Very much love to you—
Oxford.   *Affecly, Grace R. Osler*

She wrote again, six months later. Her letters were becoming less sorrowful and less concerned with her own family and events.

13 Norham Gardens, Oxford
Nov. 28th [1921]

Dear "Charlie Camac," I have had a nice little visit from your Eva and must tell you how much I liked having here [*sic*]. I hope she will be able to come again in the

Spring when Oxford is looking her best—We had a long chat one evening over the library fire and she told me the many sorrows and trials that have shadowed her young life—and spoke so tenderly of you and your companionship—and of your disappointments & grief. She seems to have such perfect and wise understanding—I have so often wanted to say something but hesitated. It has been a sincere sorrow to me that your life met with such a burden and that poor Julia should have become such a sufferer and burden to herself—I shall never forget how fresh & pretty she was when you came to the Thayer's[142] shortly after your marriage. One can only pray she may not linger long in such torture. I hardly know what to say—but you know you have my most loving sympathy. It has touched me very much to hear from Eva how you have spoken of our great friendship and your love for "our chief."

This goes with much love & sincere wishes for the future.

Affecly, Grace R. Osler

Mrs. McCagg has been here six weeks & sailed last week.

After another six months she wrote another short letter, addressing him as she now did as "Dear 'Charlie Camac.'"

13 Norham Gardens, Oxford
Wednesday [31 May 22]

Dear "Charlie Camac," Your note was a great surprise of course—but I guessed the cause of your arrival. Harriet has just been here and told me my guess was correct. My love and good wishes to Eva please. Mrs. McCagg is here and much interested of course. She goes to London in the morning—Brown's Hotel, Albermarle St. and sails for Quebec on Friday.

When your plans are all made—I shall hope to see you here—I am going away Saturday for a few days—

Affecly, Grace R. Osler

Bill Francis is living here with his wife & child working on the catalogue[143] still.

Addressing Camac for the first time as "Dear 'Charlie' " she wrote once more on July 14th, 1923, when he was in London, inviting him to come for a visit. She also wrote of unhappy events in Camac's family.

> *Care Mrs. H. P. Wright*
> *Studland, Dorset*
> *July 14th [1923]*

Dear "Charlie," I had a small gift ready to send Eva but never hearing again about the wedding I felt certain something was wrong and waited. Now I have your letter telling me what has happened—I am sure she has acted wisely if she was not perfectly satisfied—I am sorry for her but she is young and will be plucky I am sure. I am so sorry for you for I know it will grieve you to have your dear daughter suffer and you have been called upon to bear so much already. I am going away on the 16th to be away a week—can't you come on Tuesday the 24th for the night? I hope you can—I have people coming on the 25th —Hoping to hear I am

> *Affecly, Grace R. Osler*

Camac set a date for his visit, in response to which Lady Osler wrote the following note:

> *Studland (Dorset)*
> *Saturday [1923 - Summer]*

Delighted to see you Tuesday—do come on the 9:45 train from Paddington. I shall have to be out from 3 p.m. to 4:30—acting as Godmother at a christening.

> *Yours, G. R. Osler*

I return home tomorrow.

After more than a year she wrote again apologizing for the long interval between letters and with news of Harvey Cushing, family, & friends.

13 Norham Gardens, Oxford
Nov. 4, 1924

Dear "Charlie Camac," So many months have passed since I meant to write and didn't—that I am quite ashamed. I always felt disappointed about being able to do nothing for Eva when she was in Oxford—but she was so rarely here & Mrs. Robinson did so much that I was useless —I have heard from her recently and she seems happy. I hope you like her husband and are satisfied as these independent modern girls are rather difficult to keep one's finger on. We have had a busy summer here & house full. Harvey C. came the end of June—having sent his secretary Miss Shepley ahead with the manuscript of the Biography. He left the middle of August. His book is nearly finished now but will not be done for Christmas I am sorry to say.[144] I hope you like it. It has been a tremendous task for H. C. My sister has been spending the summer. I hope you were able to be at Murray Bay. Mrs. McCagg wrote how much better your wife seemed.

All good wishes, Grace R. Osler

Another year elapsed before the next brief note was written in response to a letter from Camac who was again in London, on Dec. 20, 1925 (Fig. 24).

13 Norham Gardens, Oxford
Dec. 20th [1925]

Dear Charlie Camac, I shall be so glad to see you—I hope you will not be too rushed towards your Grandfatherdom to come here for a night at least. You will get in for Christmas I suppose and you will let me know when to expect you of course. I am so happy you like the Biography—

I feel that Harvey has made a wonderful success of it. Everyone seems to agree to that. We can talk about it when you come.

A welcome and Christmas greeting to you—perhaps you can come Sunday.

Affecly, Grace R. Osler

In January, 1926, she again invited Camac to come for a visit. This was the last of Lady Osler's letters to Camac. To the end she continued to use the black-bordered stationery, although she had long since ceased to openly express her sadness.

13 Norham Gardens, Oxford, Tel. 206
Sunday [Jan. 1926]

Dear Charlie Camac, I could not hear very well what Mr. Mellor said this morning—Thinking he may have sent my letter to Paris. I send this to say I expect you here whenever you can come & for as *long* as you can stay. It will be such a pleasure to see you.

Affecly, G. R. Osler

On August 31, 1928, Lady Osler suffered a stroke and died shortly thereafter without recovering consciousness (Fig. 25).

In December, 1928, Lady Osler's sister wrote Dr. Camac from 13 Norham Gardens, closing the chapter on "The Open Arms."

13 Norham Gardens, Oxford
Dec. 1st [1928]

My dear Dr. Camac: When your note reached me here it was so long past Nov. 9th & your visit to Boston—that I did not write immediately & have again procrastinated so that December 1st is here. I am thoroughly ashamed of myself & only hope that my son wrote you that I was still in England—as he did not send on your letter to me for some time—I appreciate so much your thought & would have loved to see you had I been at home. The weeks & now months have slipped by since my sister's death & even yet this house is not quite ready to leave— We could make no move till after the books had gone to Canada & Billy Francis still had several weeks of work on them after my sister's going—She herself made all the arrangements about packing & shipping—felt that her work was done—& then never had to endure the misery of the empty shelves—It was such a blessing that it all was as it was—I have only a feeling of gratitude that she is at Peace. My niece is with me & soon we will turn homewards—having turned over to Christ Church the "Open Arms"—Perhaps you will be coming to Boston again—& I may then have the pleasure of seeing you— Ever

Yours very sincerely, Susan R. Chapin

This ends the collected correspondence.

The contents of the third volume of Camac's collection of Osler memorabilia, alluded to in the preface, attest to his devotion to his mentor and idol, "The Chief." The correspondence contained in the first two volumes helps explain this deep feeling. It also helps fill out the full life and warmth of both Sir William and Lady Osler for those who can only experience this through their biographies and writings (Fig. 26).

APPENDICES 1. & 2.

1. The Duty of the Disciple

2. The Third Notebook

The Duty of the Disciple

"In the teacher I have always valued the message of the life above the message of the pen—" *

THUS wrote the master, when he was yet among us and while it was still possible to feel, by personal contact, the inspiration of his life. Now the message of that life must be had through the medium of his pen, from which flowed such a vast treasure of counsel and encouragement. Yet there is another and more vital channel by which that "message of the life" may be conveyed. His disciples may tell of the works and influence of the master and in turn the later hearers may bear the tidings, till that spirit, known first to a comparatively small group of pupils and intimates, becomes an unquenchable torch to light the way traveled by pilgrims innumerable.

It is not the toil, the struggle, the heartache, nor yet the doctrine or creed that lives—they pass. Ideals, principles, and deeds, vitalized by the love for one's fellow-men, live on, as man's immortal self, ever reincarnated in the lives and teachings of his disciples.

So far as we know, the great Teacher of Galilee wrote but one sentence and that was traced in dust, to be soon trodden down and scattered. Yet the spirit of His life has been transmitted, through the centuries, in the lives of His disciples and by their record of His ideals, principles and deeds.

* From holograph letter, by Sir William Osler, which appeared as Frontispiece to first and second editions of "Counsels and Ideals from the Writings of William Osler," Oxford Press, London and The Riverside Press, Houghton, Mifflin & Co., Boston.

Stirring as are the writings of Osler, it may however be noticed that those who did not know him, fail to catch, from his written word, the inspiration that came from the man himself. It is the fate of all written record, unless the disciple transmit the *personal* message.

In the administration of hospitals and institutions of learning, in the establishing of museums and libraries, in methods and systems of instruction, many are fulfilling the message of his pen and thus rearing worthy memorials to his influence upon medical progress, and yet there is the greater message—the touchstone by which all these shall operate effectually—the simple, daily, personal interest in and understanding of the *individual* pupil and fellow-worker; his needs, his limitations, his aspirations, his possibilities, his trials—the exact measure of the man and a wholesome, sympathetic knowledge, usually unexpressed in words, of his conflicts and obstacles.

Few indeed are gifted with his charity, but none is so insensible as not to have felt the courage and strength which it imparted and, having known its power, few will dare withhold what little they may be able to impart.

In all the splendid efforts, in many parts of the world, to perpetuate in tablet and monument, the memory of the great teacher in medicine, I seem to hear a still, small voice, bearing *"The Message"* of his life—an imperishable monument, to be ever in the making by his disciples— a monument to "the greatest of these" which abideth and without which all else "profiteth nothing."

C. N. B. CAMAC.

The Third Notebook

THE THIRD NOTEBOOK contains miscellaneous material. In it, there is an extensive collection of newspaper clippings concerning Osler, an Osler obituary written by Camac for the "Alumni Register" of the University of Pennsylvania for February, 1920, and other obituaries. Included also is a *Guide to Corfe Castle* with the notation, in Camac's handwriting, "Visited August 1900 with Dr. and Mrs. Osler, Dr. Jacobs and little Revere Osler. The Oslers were spending the summer at Swanage."; an invitation, program of events, and correspondence relating to the First "Osler Day in Hamilton," February 27, 1935, held under the auspices of the Hamilton Academy of Medicine; and correspondence with Dr. Lewis Allis of Milwaukee, Wisconsin about the poem "When Osler Makes His Rounds."

The third notebook also contains what was saved of Camac's correspondence with Harvey Cushing, the neurosurgeon. Their acquaintance began when they both were training at Johns Hopkins. The earliest letter, handwritten in Cushing's meticulous script, is dated August 21, 1898. The last is dated November, 1933. In all there are six holographic letters and eleven typewritten ones. Included are four pages of typewritten anecdotes and recollections about Osler sent by Camac to Cushing along with some of the Osler letters for use in preparation of the biography of Osler. There also is a letter from John Fulton thanking Camac for copies of Cushing's letters which were sent to Fulton when he was writing Cushing's biography.

Notes

1. Beaman, A. G., Litt. D.: Charles Nicoll Bancker Camac (1868-1940). Bull. Hist. Med., 10: 309-313, July, 1941.

2. Davison, Wilburt C.: The Basis of Sir William Osler's Influence on Medicine. Annals of Allergy, 27: 366-372, August, 1969.

3. The Misses Gwyn referred to were Osler's nieces, daughters of his sister, Charlotte ("Chattie") and Col. C. H. Gwyn. They were, Amy, who later married Dr. Thomas McCrae; Nona, who was to marry C. Stuart; and Rachel, who later became Mrs. Almon Abbott.

4. William Broadbent, later Sir William, a British physician-friend of Osler who was said to have suggested Osler for the Regius Professorship at Oxford (Cushing, V. I, p. 649-650). He may also have been partially responsible for Osler's receiving a Baronetcy (Cushing, V. II, p. 294).

5. A form of treatment for certain types of cardiovascular disease, popularized at Bad Nauheim. It consisted of baths in warm, carbonated salt water, in conjunction with particular exercises. (Camac, C. N. B.: A visit to Bad Nauheim with the purpose of investigating the Schott Treatment for chronic heart disease. Johns Hopkins Hosp. Bull., 8: 101-106, 1897.)

6. Bad Nauheim; in central part of West Germany, north of Frankfort am Main (see #5).

7. Osler, William; On diffuse scleroderma: with special reference to diagnosis and to use of the thyroid gland extract. J. Cutan. & Genitourin. Dis., N. Y., XVI, 49; 127, 1898.

8. *Lectures on the Diagnosis of Abdominal Tumors*, New York, D. Appleton Co., 1895 (Delivered to the class of postgraduate students of Johns Hopkins University in 1893).

9. William Sydney Thayer, Osler's second resident at Johns Hopkins and Clinical Professor of Medicine after Osler's departure for Oxford.

10. Nation, Earl F.: The influence of Osler on his students. J.A.M.A., *210*: 2226-2233, 1969.

11. At St. Andrews, New Brunswick, between the meeting of the British Association for the Advancement of Science in Toronto, and a meeting of the British Medical Association in Montreal.

12. Johns Hopkins student and later a pathologist, who, as a student, while studying malaria in birds first observed the conjugation of the malarial plasmodium in the blood of crows and was thus able to explain their flagellate form. He exhibited his findings at the 1897 meeting of the British Society for the Advancement of Science, in Toronto.

13. Dr. Thomas McCrae, Osler resident who succeeded Camac; later Professor of Medicine at Jefferson College of Medicine, Philadelphia; co-author, with Osler, of several papers and of later editions of *The Principles and Practice of Medicine*, as well as of *A System of Medicine.*

14. Dr. William Gilman Thompson (1856-1927), Professor of Medicine at Cornell University, New York.

15. Louis A. Stimson (1844-1917), Professor of Surgery, Cornell University, New York.

16. Dr. J. G. Schurman, of Cornell University, New York.

17. For Izaak Walton *(The Compleat Angler)*, a favorite nickname for Revere. He was also referred to as Isaac, it has been suggested, for the son of Abraham, who sired his son when he was one-hundred years old, according to the Bible.

18. Dr. J. T. Metcalf, of New York, Camac's father-in-law.

19. In Dorset, on the South Coast of England.

20. Theodore Gaillard Thomas (1831-1903); obstetrician and gynecologist, of New York. He held the chair of Obstetrics at the College of Physicians and Surgeons from 1856 to 1879 and subsequently was Clinical Professor of Gynecology until 1890. He also was an office-partner of Camac's father-in-law. He died in Thomasville, Georgia, of a ruptured aorta.

21. Ann Arbor, where he went to address the students in December 1901.

22. In 1901 Osler served as chairman of the American Delegation to the International Congress on Tuberculosis in London. (See "Osler and tuberculosis," Nation, Earl F.: Chest, *64*: 84-87, 1973.)

23. Dr. Hunter H. McGuire (1835-1900), Professor of Surgery at the College of Physicians and Surgeons in Richmond, Virginia.

24. Henry Jones Shrapnell, who described the form and structure of the membrana tympani (Shrapnell's membrane) in 1832.

25. Several years earlier Osler gave a lecture on the life and work of Benjamin Rush. It was never published. Camac later published Rush, B.; a memorial containing travels through life on sundry incidents, etc. Lanorie, Pa., Louis A. Biddle, 1905.

26. Chauvinism in medicine, Montreal M. J., *31*: 684-699, 1902. Also Phila. M. J., *10*: 432-439, 1902.

27. *William Beaumont. A Pioneer American Physiologist.* St. Louis, 1902, 29 p. Also, J.A.M.A., *39*: 1223-1231, 1902.

28. Cushing, H.: *The Life of Sir William Osler*, V. I, p. 595.

29. Docteur Francis Munch, 17 Rue Le Verrier, Paris.

30. Miss Sarah H. Woolley, a long-time friend of Mrs. Osler.

31. *Master Word in Medicine.* Baltimore, J. Murphy & Co., 1903, 33 p. Also Brit. M. J., *2*: 1196-1200, 1903, as well as several others. Address given at Toronto, October 1, 1903.

32. Mr. & Mrs. W. L. Conyngham, old friends who lived in Wilkesbarre, Pennsylvania.

33. Mrs. Osler suffered an attack of whooping cough about this time.

34. Dr. George McClellan (1849-1913), outstanding Philadelphia anatomist and surgeon. His grandfather founded Jefferson Medical College.

35. Dr. Edward Gamaliel Janeway (1841-1911), distinguished New York pathologist and clinician.

36. John Freind. *The History of Physick; from the Time of Galen to the Beginning of the Sixteenth Century.* London, J. Walthoe, 1725-1726; 2 v. Freind was the first English historian of medicine.

37. *The Gold Headed Cane* by William Macmichael, London, John Murray, 1827.

38. Membership Committee of the New York University Club.

39. Ingersoll Lecture: Science and immortality, May 1904.

40. Degree conferred by Harvard on June 29, 1904.

41. *Science and Immortality:* Boston and New York, Houghton and Mifflin Co., 1904; The Ingersoll Lecture.

42. Dr. Henry Pickering Bowditch (1840-1911), Harvard physiologist. F. H. Garrison said of him that when he entered the Surgeon General's Library he seemed to light up the musty atmosphere as Osler may be said to have warmed it.

43. Sir John Burdon Sanderson, Oxford physiologist in whose laboratory Osler worked in 1872-73. Osler succeeded Sanderson as Regius Professor of Medicine at Oxford in 1905.

44. Brief visit to old haunts after vacation at Murray Bay.

45. The International Congress of Arts and Sciences in connection with the St. Louis Universal Exposition, September 19-25, 1904.

46. Osler's nephew; a physician; son of sister, Charlotte ("Chattie") & Col. C. H. Gwyn.

47. Mrs. Susan Chapin, of Jamaica Plain, New York.

48. The Fixed Period address, delivered in February, 1905; one of his farewell addresses for which Osler received so much bitter criticism for allegedly advocating death by chloroform for men at age 60.

49. Miss Minnie Wright Blogg, Librarian, Johns Hopkins Hospital.

50. West coast of Scotland across from the Island of Skye.

51. The original of this letter is not in the collection; only a photocopy. Attached is a cryptic note over the initials of John W. Connor, the late Librarian of the Los Angeles County Medical Association Library, to one of his librarians: "Please put with other Osler letters. Photocopy of original offered by Henry Schuman, price $112.50, returned 7/29/60."

52. The book was finally printed by Horace Hart of the Oxford University Press. Houghton Mifflin handled it in the United States.

53. Lord Lovatt's estate in North Berwick which Mr. Henry Phipps (Phipps Institute, Philadelphia; Phipps Psychiatric Clinic, Johns Hopkins) often took over for the summer and where the Oslers visited several times (Cushing, V. I, p. 615).

54. Island of Skye, off northwest coast of Scotland.

55. Someone, presumably Camac, penciled " '04 or '05" after August 31st. However, events referred to suggest that the year must have been 1906.

56. Osler's niece, later Mrs. Thomas McCrae.

57. Charlotte (sister "Chattie") E. Gwyn, wife of Col. C. H. Gwyn.

58. Thomas Willis; William Heberden; Matthew Baillie.

59. Cushing, *The Life of Sir William Osler*, V. I, p. 677.

60. Richard Lee MacDonnell: *Counsels and Ideals from the Writings of William Osler*, C. N. B. Camac, p. 44; from N. Y. Med. J., 1891.

61. Dr. H. B. Jacobs, of Baltimore, commissioned Frédéric Charles Victor de Vernon, of Paris, to produce a sculpture, in the form of a plaque, of Osler in 1903. Copies subsequently were made for members of the Charaka Club, of New York. (See Courville, Cyril B., Sir William Osler and his portraits, Bull. Hist. Med., 23: 353-378 [footnote, p. 367], 1949.)

62. Club of New York Bibliophiles, most of whom were physicians.

63. International Tuberculosis Congress. Emile Loubet gave a banquet and reception at the Élysée.

64. Mr. Horace Hart, printer to Oxford University.

65. To say good-bye to his mother.

66. Miss Olean Humpton, Osler's secretary.

67. *Lives of British Physicians*, published by William Macmichael in 1830: It consists of eighteen biographies, six of which were written by Macmichael himself (Linacre, Caius, Harvey, Sir Thomas Browne, Sydenham and Radcliffe.)

68. T. B. Futcher, one of a series of Canadian physicians who gravitated from Toronto to Johns Hopkins for postgraduate training under Osler. He remained to become a Professor of Medicine.

69. Cushing, H.: *The Life of Sir William Osler*, V. II, p. 58. Also, Nation, Earl F.: Sir William Osler, the Master of Ewelme. Canad. M. A. J., *109*: 1128-1132, 1973.

70. Joseph Lister, the first Baron. See Cushing, V. II, p. 308.

71. Hamilton, Ontario, where Osler did a locum tenens in 1874 before returning to McGill. Some of his old friends and associates still resided there.

72. Featherstone misspelled.

73. The estate of Osler's brother, Sir Edmund Boyd Osler.

74. At this time Osler's mother had six living children, 26 grandchildren, and 21 greatgrandchildren. The discrepancy in Osler's number is not clear.

75. W. B. Saunders, Co. who published *Epoch Making Contributions to Medicine, Surgery and the Allied Sciences*.

76. "Sir Thomas Browne," address delivered before Guy's Hospital, London, October 12, 1905, and published in various places. See Maude E. Abbott's *Classified Bibliography of Sir William Osler*, Montreal, The Medical Museum, McGill University, Sect. IV, 1905.

77. Dr. William H. Welch, one of the "Big Four" at Johns Hopkins.

78. The Oxford University Press.

79. Thomas McCrae, T. B. Futcher, L. F. Barker, and T. R. Boggs, all of Johns Hopkins.

80. *An Alabama Student and Other Biographical Essays*, Oxford University Press, 1908.

81. Apparently not published.

82. Christ Church, Oxford, of which Osler was a "student" and a member of the governing body. Here Robert Burton's library was housed.

83. Two of Henry Bowditch's five daughters. See #42.

84. Henry Frowde, Publisher of the Oxford Press, in London; succeeded by Mr. Humphrey Milford.

85. *Epoch Making Contributions to Medicine, Surgery, and the Allied Sciences*, by C. N. B. Camac. Philadelphia, W. B. Saunders Co., 1909.

86. Izaak Walton: author of *The Compleat Angler*, first published in 1653. Revere was a devoted fisherman. So was often referred to as "Isaac Walton" or "Ike." See #17 for another explanation for the nickname.

87. Osler's college at Oxford, founded in 1525, referred to as "The House" by the men, Osler says.

88. Brasenose College, of Oxford University, where Robert Burton was a commoner in 1593. He was elected a student at Christ Church six years later.

89. Bodleian Library (1598), of Oxford, of which Osler was a Curator.

90. Lord Curzon of Kedleston, Chancellor of the University, raised an Oxford University endowment fund through an appeal made in 1907. Cushing credits Osler with having something to do with the effort (V. II, p. 70).

91. John Barnard Swett Jackson (1806-1879), pioneer pathologist, Shattuck Professor of Morbid Anatomy at Harvard from 1854 to 1879. Osler observed his course in pathology in 1877.

92. *The Collected Papers of Joseph Baron Lister*, two volumes, Oxford, 1909.

93. C. N. B. Camac, *Epoch Making Contributions to Medicine, Surgery, and the Allied Sciences*, W. B. Saunders & Co., 1909.

94. To attend the annual German Kongress fur Innere Medizin in the company of his friend and former pupil, Dr. Joseph H. Pratt, of Baltimore.

95. *Thomas Linacre*, Cambridge University Press, 1908.

96. Seventh edition of *Principles and Practice of Medicine*, which W. W. Francis saw through the press.

97. International Congress on Tuberculosis, Washington, D. C., September 21, 1908.

98. The Spa at Bad Nauheim (see #5 & #6).

99. Michael Servetus, the martyr, admired by Osler. See Osler's *Michael Servetus*, London, Henry Frowde, Oxford University Press, 1909.

100. *Epoch Making Contributions to Medicine, Surgery, and the Allied Sciences*, Philadelphia and London, W. B. Saunders Co., 1909.

101. Dr. Henry D. Nicoll, Camac's brother-in-law, with whom he practiced.

102. Lister, Joseph, 1st Baron (1827-1912). *The Collected Papers of Joseph Baron Lister*. In 2 volumes, 1909.

103. Palmer Howard's younger son who trained at McGill and under Osler later at Johns Hopkins.

104. Dr. W. W. Francis, Osler's first-cousin-once-removed; later Osler Librarian at McGill.

105. Marjorie Howard, daughter of Osler's early Canadian friend, Palmer Howard. She became Mrs. T. B. Futcher.

106. Large New York bookstore.

107. The former Miss Mabel Tremaine who Osler saw as a patient in 1900 and who became a close lifelong friend of the family.

108. Bliss Perry (1860-1954), Professor of English, Harvard, 1907-1930. He wrote *Walt Whitman* in 1906.

109. Joseph Hilaire Pierre Belloc (1870-1953). French-born English writer who enjoyed and wrote about travel, among many other things.

110. Osler served as president of the National Association for the Prevention of Tuberculosis in 1910. The meeting was held in Edinburgh. It was here that Osler delivered his memorable address, *Man's Redemption of Man*; London, Constable & Co., 1910.

111. Man's redemption of man, Am. Mag., N. Y., 71: 1910-1911, 246-252. Also New York, P. B. Hoeber, 1913, 63 p.

112. "Charlie" Locke, one of Osler's childhood friends, one of "Barrie's Bad Boys," a trio which included Osler and Ned Milburn.

113. Sir Edmund Boyd Osler.

114. The great obelisk at Karnak in upper Egypt.

115. Silliman Lectures at Yale University, on "The Evolution of Modern Medicine," beginning on April 21, 1913. The lectures were published by Yale University Press, New Haven, in 1921. The lectures were preceded on Sunday, April 20, by a lay sermon, "A Way of Life," delivered before the students of Yale in Woolsey Hall. This talk was completed only on the morning of delivery.

116. Phipps Psychiatric Clinic, where, on April 16, 1913, Osler opened the ceremonies with his lecture, "Specialism in the General Hospital."

117. Opening of Phipps Psychiatric Institute, referred to in the previous note.

118. *Counsels and Ideals from the Writings of William Osler*, by Camac.

119. The XVIIth International Congress, under the presidency of Sir Thomas Barlow, August 6 to 12, 1913. Osler had attended the one held in London thirty-two years before in the company of Palmer Howard, of McGill.

120. Dr. George Cheever Shattuck, scion of a long line of eminent Boston physicians.

121. Cushing became a fellow and gave one of the three principal addresses. His topic was, "Realignments in Greater Medicine; their effect upon surgery and the influence of surgery upon them."

122. Dr. Theodore Bernard Sachs (1868-1916), of Chicago. He had a great interest in tuberculosis. He committed suicide over his frustration with the City administration.

123. Possibly Dr. Henry P. Stearns (1828-1905), of Connecticut; Lecturer at Yale on mental diseases.

124. Camac's sister, Elizabeth, who resided in London and who was married to Sir Frank Mellor, a noted English lawyer.

125. A newspaper clipping is enclosed appealing for American assistance in connection with care of European refugees from the war.

126. Dr. H. W. Beal who was in charge of the American Hospital at Paignton, England.

127. The American Womens War Relief Fund organized and maintained an auxiliary hospital of 250 beds at Paignton, England.

128. Dr. J. F. Page.

129. Probably Richard Le Galliene's *Religion of a Literary Man*, London, 1893.

130. Paratyphoid patients.

131. Osler student at Johns Hopkins who remained under Barker doing bacteriology.

132. Herbert Putnam.

133. Dr. William H. Welch, pathologist, Johns Hopkins; Dr. William S. Thayer, Professor of Medicine, Johns Hopkins; Dr. Lewellys F. Barker, Osler's successor as Chief, Johns Hopkins; Mr. Henry M. Hurd, Superintendent, Johns Hopkins Hospital; Dr. Harry M. Thomas, neurologist, Johns Hopkins; Dr. Thomas B. Futcher, another of the Canadians who trained under Osler and remained at Johns Hopkins.

134. Leonard L. Mackall, with whom Osler often corresponded on bibliophilic matters; Dr. Harvey Cushing, Osler's biographer; Worthington Ford, of the Library of Congress; Dr. Thomas McCrae, Osler's student and later co-author.

135. Sotheby's auction rooms, in Wellington Street.

136. Dr. Norman Gwyn's illness was thought possibly to be paratyphoid.

137. Dr. Archibald Malloch who was to assist in the preparation of the *Bibliotheca Osleriana* and later to become Librarian of the New York Academy of Medicine.

138. Dr. W. W. Francis, Osler's first-cousin-once-removed, sometimes referred to as his nephew. He spent much time in the Osler household, was principally responsible for the *Bibliotheca Osleriana*, and remained the Osler Librarian at McGill until his death.

139. Canadian Army Medical Corps. There were troubles and tensions between the Canadians and British which bothered Osler a great deal. (See Cushing, V. II, p. 538.)

140. William Thompson Sedwick (1855-1921). Biologist and epidemiologist who trained at Yale and Johns Hopkins and for many years headed the Department of Biology and Public Health at Massachusetts Institute of Technology.

141. Second edition of *Counsels and Ideals from the Writings of William Osler*, London, Oxford Press, January, 1921.

142. Dr. William S. Thayer, of Baltimore (see #9).

143. *Bibliotheca Osleriana*, Oxford, at the Clarendon Press, 1929.

144. *The Life of Sir William Osler*, Oxford, The Clarendon Press, 1925.